weightwatchers

Plan&
Track

weightwatchers

Plan &
Track

Use this book to plan for your success, as well as track your *PointsPlus*® values.

Use **My Week at a Glance** to anticipate what's coming for the week. Think about what you'll eat, and how you'll get your activity in. Consider the obstacles you may face. The tools in **My Weekly To Do List** will help you plan how you'll tackle them.

On the daily pages, record the food you eat and your activity *PointsPlus* values earned and used. Whether you are tracking against your daily *PointsPlus* Target or following Simple Start or Simply Filling, you can check off your weekly *PointsPlus* Allowance as you use it to see what you have left at a glance. Over time, flip back at past weeks to determine what made them successful or not-so-successful.

For an illustration of how to use this book, review the sample pages.

sample pages

My Week at a Glance

	Day 1	Day 2	Day 3
What's coming this week		PJs baseball playoffs	
Breakfast	Cereal & skim milk	Cereal & skim milk	Cheese stick, banana
Lunch	Turkey sandwich from Joe's Deli	Grilled chicken salad	Turkey sandwich from Joe's Deli
Dinner	Sirloin steak salad	Dinner at the game!	Chicken & Corn recipe plus veg.
Snacks	Nuts, banana, apple, pudding for dessert	Frozen yogourt for dessert	Nuts, fruit
My Activity Plan	Sculpting video before work		6 pm Zumba class
Weekly PointsPlus® Allowance Allotted	2	9	2

sample pages

Day 4	Day 5	Day 6	Day 7
		Kids' Halloween Festival	Gina's party
Orange, egg whites	Orange, egg whites	Cereal & skim milk	Toasted bagel w/butter OJ
Grilled chicken salad	Slice of pizza	Turkey sandwich from Joe's Deli	Salad & fish
Turkey burger, roll Salad	Salmon, oven "fries", green veggies	Halloween Party	Party!
Banana, apple, cheese stick	Frozen yogourt for dessert – fruit, fruit, fruit!!!		Cake!
Cardio machine 30 min. before work		9 am Walk 5 km	
		15	15

sample pages

My Weekly To Do List

notes

- dry cleaner

- pick up pumpkins for festival
- carve on Friday

- register for Zumba — 6pm on Tuesday

Dishes to Make:

Name of Dish: _Steak Salad_

Where to find it: _Allrecipes.com_

Name of Dish: _Chicken & Corn Salad_

Where to find it: _Master Your Meals_
Page 60

Name of Dish: _Oven Fries_

Where to find it: _weightwatchers.ca_

Name of Dish: _Grilled Salmon_

Where to find it: _In my head!_

Name of Dish: _____

Where to find it: _____

Date: 10 / 21 / 14

Groceries:

2 potatoes

2 bags romaine

Apples

Bananas

Fresh parsley

Case of seltzer

450g (1 lb) chicken

breast

1% milk

Dozen eggs

Pumpkins?

tip "All you need is love. But a little chocolate now and then doesn't hurt." — **Charles M. Schulz**

sample pages

	PointsPlus® value		POWER FOODS ▲
	+/−	balance	
My daily **PointsPlus** Target:		26	
Sandwich: Lt w-g English muffin with			
1 slice Can. bacon, tomato, 1 slice of f/f cheese	5	21	✓
250ml (1 cup) cantaloupe	0	21	✓
Salad: greens, tomatoes, strawberries,			
15ml (1 Tbsp) walnuts, 5ml (1 tsp) oil	2	19	✓
Flounder 170g (6 oz), cooked with 10ml (2 tsp) olive oil	6	13	✓
1 large apple	0	13	✓
1 piece strawberry shortcake—Gina's party	8	5	
Tacos: 2 corn tortillas, ff salsa, black beans			
55g (2 oz) chicken, and 60ml (4 Tbsp) cheddar	8	−3	✓
250ml (1 cup) asparagus	0	−3	✓
250ml (1 cup) light yogourt	3	−6	✓
1 medium peach	0	−6	✓
250ml (1 cup) frozen strawberries	0	−6	✓
My remaining daily **PointsPlus** Target total:		−6	
Activity **PointsPlus** values earned:		0	
Activity **PointsPlus** values used:		0	
Weekly **PointsPlus** Allowance used:		6	
My Activity Today:		Duration	

GOOD HEALTH GUIDELINES

HAVE DAILY: LIQUIDS ☑ ☑ ☑ ☑ ☑ ☑
HEALTHY OILS ☑ ☑
MULTIVITAMIN ☑

ALSO REMEMBER: Watch your intake of sodium, added sugar, alcohol

EAT WEIGHT WATCHERS POWER FOODS

FRUITS & VEGGIES ☑ ☑ ☑ ☑ ☐ ☐ ☐ ☐
NON-FAT & LOW-FAT DAIRY ☑ ☑ ☐
WHOLE GRAINS   LEAN PROTEINS

Non-fat dairy options are Power Foods and better for weight loss.

sample pages

Weekly Wrap-up

This week I lost/gained: Lost 1.2 lbs!

Meeting notes:

- huge glass of seltzer with lemon when I wake up & before
  lunch helps.

This week I learned:

Didn't have time for early workout. Lay out sneakers and
clothes the night before.

> Check off weekly *PointsPlus* Allowance as you use it

My Weekly *PointsPlus*® Allowance

49 48 47 46 45 44 43 42 41 40 39 38 37 36 35 34 33 32 31 30

29 28 27 26 25 24 23 22 21 20 19 18 17 16 15 14 13 12 11 10

9 8 7 6 5 4 3 2 1

> Circle your weekly activity *PointsPlus* goal and check off activity *PointsPlus* values as they're earned and used

My Weekly Activity *PointsPlus* Values

EARNED	1	2	3	4	5	6	7	8	9	10	11	12	13	14
USED	1	2	3	4	5	6	7	8	9	10	11	12	13	14
EARNED	15	16	17	18	19	20	21	22	23	24	25	26	27	28
USED	15	16	17	18	19	20	21	22	23	24	25	26	27	28
EARNED	29	30	31	32	33	34	35	36	37	38	39	40	41	42
USED	29	30	31	32	33	34	35	36	37	38	39	40	41	42

Planning and Tracking Pages

My Week at a Glance

	Day 1	Day 2	Day 3
What's coming this week			
Breakfast			
Lunch			
Dinner			
Snacks			
My Activity Plan			
Weekly *PointsPlus*® Allowance Allotted			

Date: ____ / ____ / ____

Day 4	Day 5	Day 6	Day 7

My Weekly To Do List

notes

Dishes to Make:

Name of Dish: _____

_____

Where to find it: _____

_____

Name of Dish: _____

_____

Where to find it: _____

_____

Name of Dish: _____

_____

Where to find it: _____

_____

Name of Dish: _____

_____

Where to find it: _____

_____

Name of Dish: _____

_____

Where to find it: _____

_____

Groceries:

_____   _____
_____   _____
_____   _____
_____   _____
_____   _____
_____   _____
_____   _____
_____   _____
_____   _____
_____   _____
_____   _____
_____   _____
_____   _____
_____   _____
_____   _____
_____   _____
_____   _____
_____   _____
_____   _____

tip "The secret to staying young is to live honestly, eat slowly, and lie about your age." — **Lucille Ball**

Day 1

	PointsPlus® value		POWER FOODS ▲
	+/−	balance	
My daily *PointsPlus* Target:			
My remaining daily *PointsPlus* Target total:			▲
Activity *PointsPlus* values earned:			
Activity *PointsPlus* values used:			
Weekly *PointsPlus* Allowance used:			

My Activity Today:	Duration

GOOD HEALTH GUIDELINES _____

HAVE DAILY: **LIQUIDS** ☐ ☐ ☐ ☐ ☐ ☐
HEALTHY OILS ☐ ☐
MULTIVITAMIN ☐
ALSO REMEMBER: Watch your intake of sodium, added sugar, alcohol

EAT WEIGHT WATCHERS POWER FOODS _____

FRUITS & VEGGIES ☐ ☐ ☐ ☐ ☐ ☐ ☐ ☐ ☐
NON-FAT & LOW-FAT DAIRY ☐ ☐ ☐
WHOLE GRAINS **LEAN PROTEINS**
Non-fat dairy options are Power Foods and better for weight loss.

Day 2

	PointsPlus® value		POWER FOODS
	+/−	balance	▲
My daily **PointsPlus** Target:			
My remaining daily **PointsPlus** Target total:			▲
Activity **PointsPlus** values earned:			
Activity **PointsPlus** values used:			
Weekly **PointsPlus** Allowance used:			

My Activity Today:	Duration

GOOD HEALTH GUIDELINES

HAVE DAILY: LIQUIDS ☐ ☐ ☐ ☐ ☐ ☐
HEALTHY OILS ☐ ☐
MULTIVITAMIN ☐

ALSO REMEMBER: Watch your intake of sodium, added sugar, alcohol

EAT WEIGHT WATCHERS POWER FOODS

FRUITS & VEGGIES ☐ ☐ ☐ ☐ ☐ ☐ ☐ ☐ ☐
NON-FAT & LOW-FAT DAIRY ☐ ☐ ☐
WHOLE GRAINS   LEAN PROTEINS

Non-fat dairy options are Power Foods and better for weight loss.

Date: /   /

Day 3

	PointsPlus® value		POWER FOODS ▲
	+/−	balance	
My daily *PointsPlus* Target:			
My remaining daily *PointsPlus* Target total:			▲
Activity *PointsPlus* values earned:			
Activity *PointsPlus* values used:			
Weekly *PointsPlus* Allowance used:			

My Activity Today:	Duration

GOOD HEALTH GUIDELINES

HAVE DAILY: LIQUIDS ☐ ☐ ☐ ☐ ☐ ☐
HEALTHY OILS ☐ ☐
MULTIVITAMIN ☐

ALSO REMEMBER: Watch your intake of sodium, added sugar, alcohol

EAT WEIGHT WATCHERS POWER FOODS

FRUITS & VEGGIES ☐ ☐ ☐ ☐ ☐ ☐ ☐ ☐ ☐
NON-FAT & LOW-FAT DAIRY ☐ ☐ ☐
WHOLE GRAINS   LEAN PROTEINS

Non-fat dairy options are Power Foods and better for weight loss.

Day 4

Date: /   /

	PointsPlus® value		POWER FOODS
	+/−	balance	▲
My daily **PointsPlus** Target:			
My remaining daily **PointsPlus** Target total:			▲
Activity **PointsPlus** values earned:			
Activity **PointsPlus** values used:			
Weekly **PointsPlus** Allowance used:			

My Activity Today:	Duration

GOOD HEALTH GUIDELINES

HAVE DAILY: LIQUIDS ☐ ☐ ☐ ☐ ☐ ☐
               HEALTHY OILS ☐ ☐
               MULTIVITAMIN ☐

ALSO REMEMBER: Watch your intake of sodium, added sugar, alcohol

EAT WEIGHT WATCHERS POWER FOODS

FRUITS & VEGGIES ☐ ☐ ☐ ☐ ☐ ☐ ☐ ☐
NON-FAT & LOW-FAT DAIRY ☐ ☐ ☐
WHOLE GRAINS   LEAN PROTEINS

Non-fat dairy options are Power Foods and better for weight loss.

Day 5

	PointsPlus® value		POWER FOODS ▲
	+/–	balance	
My daily **PointsPlus** Target:			

My remaining daily **PointsPlus** Target total:		▲
Activity **PointsPlus** values earned:		
Activity **PointsPlus** values used:		
Weekly **PointsPlus** Allowance used:		

My Activity Today:	Duration

GOOD HEALTH GUIDELINES

HAVE DAILY: LIQUIDS ☐ ☐ ☐ ☐ ☐ ☐
           HEALTHY OILS ☐ ☐
           MULTIVITAMIN ☐

ALSO REMEMBER: Watch your intake of sodium, added sugar, alcohol

EAT WEIGHT WATCHERS POWER FOODS

FRUITS & VEGGIES ☐ ☐ ☐ ☐ ☐ ☐ ☐ ☐ ☐
NON-FAT & LOW-FAT DAIRY ☐ ☐ ☐
WHOLE GRAINS   LEAN PROTEINS

Non-fat dairy options are Power Foods and better for weight loss.

Day 6

	PointsPlus® value		POWER FOODS ▲
	+/−	balance	
My daily **PointsPlus** Target:			
My remaining daily **PointsPlus** Target total:			▲
Activity **PointsPlus** values earned:			
Activity **PointsPlus** values used:			
Weekly **PointsPlus** Allowance used:			

My Activity Today:	Duration

GOOD HEALTH GUIDELINES

HAVE DAILY: LIQUIDS ☐ ☐ ☐ ☐ ☐ ☐
HEALTHY OILS ☐ ☐
MULTIVITAMIN ☐

ALSO REMEMBER: Watch your intake of sodium, added sugar, alcohol

EAT WEIGHT WATCHERS POWER FOODS

FRUITS & VEGGIES ☐ ☐ ☐ ☐ ☐ ☐ ☐ ☐ ☐
NON-FAT & LOW-FAT DAIRY ☐ ☐ ☐
WHOLE GRAINS   LEAN PROTEINS

Non-fat dairy options are Power Foods and better for weight loss.

Day 7

	PointsPlus® value		POWER FOODS ▲
	+/−	balance	
My daily **PointsPlus** Target:			
My remaining daily **PointsPlus** Target total:			▲
Activity **PointsPlus** values earned:			
Activity **PointsPlus** values used:			
Weekly **PointsPlus** Allowance used:			

My Activity Today:	Duration

GOOD HEALTH GUIDELINES

HAVE DAILY: LIQUIDS ☐☐☐☐☐☐
HEALTHY OILS ☐☐
MULTIVITAMIN ☐

ALSO REMEMBER: Watch your intake of sodium, added sugar, alcohol

EAT WEIGHT WATCHERS POWER FOODS

FRUITS & VEGGIES ☐☐☐☐☐☐☐☐☐
NON-FAT & LOW-FAT DAIRY ☐☐☐
WHOLE GRAINS   LEAN PROTEINS

Non-fat dairy options are Power Foods and better for weight loss.

Weekly Wrap-up

This week I lost/gained: _____

Meeting notes:

_____

_____

_____

_____

This week I learned:

_____

_____

_____

My Weekly *PointsPlus*® Allowance

49 **48** **47** **46** **45** **44** **43** **42** **41** **40** **39** **38** **37** **36** **35** **34** **33** **32** **31** **30**

29 **28** **27** **26** **25** **24** **23** **22** **21** **20** **19** **18** **17** **16** **15** **14** **13** **12** **11** **10**

9 **8** **7** **6** **5** **4** **3** **2** **1**

My Weekly Activity *PointsPlus* Values

EARNED	1	2	3	4	5	6	7	8	9	10	11	12	13	14
USED	1	2	3	4	5	6	7	8	9	10	11	12	13	14
EARNED	15	16	17	18	19	20	21	22	23	24	25	26	27	28
USED	15	16	17	18	19	20	21	22	23	24	25	26	27	28
EARNED	29	30	31	32	33	34	35	36	37	38	39	40	41	42
USED	29	30	31	32	33	34	35	36	37	38	39	40	41	42

My Week at a Glance

	Day 1	Day 2	Day 3
What's coming this week			
Breakfast			
Lunch			
Dinner			
Snacks			
My Activity Plan			
Weekly *PointsPlus*® Allowance Allotted			

Date: _____ / _____ / _____

Day 4	Day 5	Day 6	Day 7

My Weekly To Do List

notes

Dishes to Make:

Name of Dish: _____

_____

Where to find it: _____

_____

Name of Dish: _____

_____

Where to find it: _____

_____

Name of Dish: _____

_____

Where to find it: _____

_____

Name of Dish: _____

_____

Where to find it: _____

_____

Name of Dish: _____

_____

Where to find it: _____

_____

Date: /   /

Groceries:

_____   _____
_____   _____
_____   _____
_____   _____
_____   _____
_____   _____
_____   _____
_____   _____
_____   _____
_____   _____
_____   _____
_____   _____
_____   _____
_____   _____
_____   _____
_____   _____
_____   _____
_____   _____

tip On the inside cover of this book, write down your top three reasons for wanting to lose weight. Refer to this list often.

Day 1

	PointsPlus® value		POWER FOODS
	+/−	balance	▲
My daily **PointsPlus** Target:			
My remaining daily **PointsPlus** Target total:			▲
Activity **PointsPlus** values earned:			
Activity **PointsPlus** values used:			
Weekly **PointsPlus** Allowance used:			
My Activity Today:		Duration	

GOOD HEALTH GUIDELINES

HAVE DAILY: LIQUIDS ☐ ☐ ☐ ☐ ☐ ☐
HEALTHY OILS ☐ ☐
MULTIVITAMIN ☐

ALSO REMEMBER: Watch your intake of sodium, added sugar, alcohol

EAT WEIGHT WATCHERS POWER FOODS

FRUITS & VEGGIES ☐ ☐ ☐ ☐ ☐ ☐ ☐ ☐ ☐
NON-FAT & LOW-FAT DAIRY ☐ ☐ ☐
WHOLE GRAINS   LEAN PROTEINS

Non-fat dairy options are Power Foods and better for weight loss.

Day 2

	PointsPlus® value		POWER FOODS
	+/−	balance	▲
My daily **PointsPlus** Target:			
My remaining daily **PointsPlus** Target total:			▲
Activity **PointsPlus** values earned:			
Activity **PointsPlus** values used:			
Weekly **PointsPlus** Allowance used:			
My Activity Today:		Duration	

GOOD HEALTH GUIDELINES

HAVE DAILY: LIQUIDS ☐ ☐ ☐ ☐ ☐ ☐
HEALTHY OILS ☐ ☐
MULTIVITAMIN ☐

ALSO REMEMBER: Watch your intake of sodium, added sugar, alcohol

EAT WEIGHT WATCHERS POWER FOODS

FRUITS & VEGGIES ☐ ☐ ☐ ☐ ☐ ☐ ☐ ☐ ☐
NON-FAT & LOW-FAT DAIRY ☐ ☐ ☐
WHOLE GRAINS   LEAN PROTEINS

Non-fat dairy options are Power Foods and better for weight loss.

	PointsPlus® value		POWER FOODS
	+/−	balance	▲
My daily *PointsPlus* Target:			
My remaining daily *PointsPlus* Target total:			▲
Activity *PointsPlus* values earned:			
Activity *PointsPlus* values used:			
Weekly *PointsPlus* Allowance used:			
My Activity Today:		Duration	

GOOD HEALTH GUIDELINES

HAVE DAILY: LIQUIDS ☐☐☐☐☐☐
HEALTHY OILS ☐☐
MULTIVITAMIN ☐
ALSO REMEMBER: Watch your intake of sodium, added sugar, alcohol

EAT WEIGHT WATCHERS POWER FOODS

FRUITS & VEGGIES ☐☐☐☐☐☐☐☐☐
NON-FAT & LOW-FAT DAIRY ☐☐☐
WHOLE GRAINS   LEAN PROTEINS
Non-fat dairy options are Power Foods and better for weight loss.

Day 4

	PointsPlus® value		POWER FOODS
	+/−	balance	▲
My daily **PointsPlus** Target:			
My remaining daily **PointsPlus** Target total:			▲
Activity **PointsPlus** values earned:			
Activity **PointsPlus** values used:			
Weekly **PointsPlus** Allowance used:			
My Activity Today:		Duration	

GOOD HEALTH GUIDELINES

HAVE DAILY: LIQUIDS ☐ ☐ ☐ ☐ ☐ ☐
HEALTHY OILS ☐ ☐
MULTIVITAMIN ☐

ALSO REMEMBER: Watch your intake of sodium, added sugar, alcohol

EAT WEIGHT WATCHERS POWER FOODS

FRUITS & VEGGIES ☐ ☐ ☐ ☐ ☐ ☐ ☐ ☐ ☐
NON-FAT & LOW-FAT DAIRY ☐ ☐ ☐
WHOLE GRAINS LEAN PROTEINS

Non-fat dairy options are Power Foods and better for weight loss.

Date: / /

Day 5

	PointsPlus® value		POWER FOODS ▲
	+/−	balance	
My daily *PointsPlus* Target:			
My remaining daily *PointsPlus* Target total:			▲
Activity *PointsPlus* values earned:			
Activity *PointsPlus* values used:			
Weekly *PointsPlus* Allowance used:			
My Activity Today:		Duration	

GOOD HEALTH GUIDELINES

HAVE DAILY: LIQUIDS ☐☐☐☐☐☐
HEALTHY OILS ☐☐
MULTIVITAMIN ☐

ALSO REMEMBER: Watch your intake of sodium, added sugar, alcohol

EAT WEIGHT WATCHERS POWER FOODS

FRUITS & VEGGIES ☐☐☐☐☐☐☐☐☐
NON-FAT & LOW-FAT DAIRY ☐☐☐
WHOLE GRAINS LEAN PROTEINS

Non-fat dairy options are Power Foods and better for weight loss.

Day 6

2 week

	PointsPlus® value		POWER FOODS ▲
	+/−	balance	
My daily **PointsPlus** Target:			
My remaining daily **PointsPlus** Target total:			
Activity **PointsPlus** values earned:			
Activity **PointsPlus** values used:			
Weekly **PointsPlus** Allowance used:			

My Activity Today:	Duration

GOOD HEALTH GUIDELINES

HAVE DAILY: LIQUIDS ☐ ☐ ☐ ☐ ☐ ☐
　　　　　　 HEALTHY OILS ☐ ☐
　　　　　　 MULTIVITAMIN ☐

ALSO REMEMBER: Watch your intake of sodium, added sugar, alcohol

EAT WEIGHT WATCHERS POWER FOODS

FRUITS & VEGGIES ☐ ☐ ☐ ☐ ☐ ☐ ☐ ☐ ☐
NON-FAT & LOW-FAT DAIRY ☐ ☐ ☐
WHOLE GRAINS　LEAN PROTEINS

Non-fat dairy options are Power Foods and better for weight loss.

Day 7

	PointsPlus® value		POWER FOODS ▲
	+/−	balance	
My daily PointsPlus Target:			
My remaining daily PointsPlus Target total:			▲
Activity PointsPlus values earned:			
Activity PointsPlus values used:			
Weekly PointsPlus Allowance used:			

My Activity Today:	Duration

GOOD HEALTH GUIDELINES _____

HAVE DAILY: **LIQUIDS** ☐ ☐ ☐ ☐ ☐ ☐
HEALTHY OILS ☐ ☐
MULTIVITAMIN ☐

ALSO REMEMBER: Watch your intake of sodium, added sugar, alcohol

EAT WEIGHT WATCHERS POWER FOODS _____

FRUITS & VEGGIES ☐ ☐ ☐ ☐ ☐ ☐ ☐ ☐ ☐
NON-FAT & LOW-FAT DAIRY ☐ ☐ ☐
WHOLE GRAINS   LEAN PROTEINS

Non-fat dairy options are Power Foods and better for weight loss.

Weekly Wrap-up

This week I lost/gained: _____

Meeting notes:

_____

_____

_____

_____

This week I learned:

_____

_____

_____

My Weekly *PointsPlus*® Allowance

49 48 47 46 45 44 43 42 41 40 39 38 37 36 35 34 33 32 31 30

29 28 27 26 25 24 23 22 21 20 19 18 17 16 15 14 13 12 11 10

9 8 7 6 5 4 3 2 1

My Weekly Activity *PointsPlus* Values

EARNED	1	2	3	4	5	6	7	8	9	10	11	12	13	14
USED	1	2	3	4	5	6	7	8	9	10	11	12	13	14
EARNED	15	16	17	18	19	20	21	22	23	24	25	26	27	28
USED	15	16	17	18	19	20	21	22	23	24	25	26	27	28
EARNED	29	30	31	32	33	34	35	36	37	38	39	40	41	42
USED	29	30	31	32	33	34	35	36	37	38	39	40	41	42

My Week at a Glance

	Day 1	Day 2	Day 3
What's coming this week			
Breakfast			
Lunch			
Dinner			
Snacks			
My Activity Plan			
Weekly *PointsPlus*® Allowance Allotted			

Day 4	Day 5	Day 6	Day 7

My Weekly To Do List

notes

Dishes to Make:

Name of Dish: _____

_____

Where to find it: _____

_____

Name of Dish: _____

_____

Where to find it: _____

_____

Name of Dish: _____

_____

Where to find it: _____

_____

Name of Dish: _____

_____

Where to find it: _____

_____

Name of Dish: _____

_____

Where to find it: _____

_____

Groceries:

_____	_____
_____	_____
_____	_____
_____	_____
_____	_____
_____	_____
_____	_____
_____	_____
_____	_____
_____	_____
_____	_____
_____	_____
_____	_____
_____	_____
_____	_____
_____	_____

 tip Have a back-up plan for days that your plans change. Know your "go-to" meal options and their *PointsPlus* values so you're always in control. Some examples: microwavable meals and better-for-you takeout.

	PointsPlus® value		POWER FOODS ▲
	+/−	balance	
My daily **PointsPlus** Target:			
My remaining daily **PointsPlus** Target total:			▲
Activity **PointsPlus** values earned:			
Activity **PointsPlus** values used:			
Weekly **PointsPlus** Allowance used:			

My Activity Today:	Duration

GOOD HEALTH GUIDELINES

HAVE DAILY: LIQUIDS ☐ ☐ ☐ ☐ ☐
HEALTHY OILS ☐ ☐
MULTIVITAMIN ☐

ALSO REMEMBER: Watch your intake of sodium, added sugar, alcohol

EAT WEIGHT WATCHERS POWER FOODS

FRUITS & VEGGIES ☐ ☐ ☐ ☐ ☐ ☐ ☐ ☐
NON-FAT & LOW-FAT DAIRY ☐ ☐ ☐
WHOLE GRAINS   LEAN PROTEINS

Non-fat dairy options are Power Foods and better for weight loss.

| | PointsPlus® value | | POWER FOODS |
	+/−	balance	▲
My daily **PointsPlus** Target:			
My remaining daily **PointsPlus** Target total:			▲
Activity **PointsPlus** values earned:			
Activity **PointsPlus** values used:			
Weekly **PointsPlus** Allowance used:			
My Activity Today:		Duration	

GOOD HEALTH GUIDELINES

HAVE DAILY: LIQUIDS ☐ ☐ ☐ ☐ ☐ ☐
HEALTHY OILS ☐ ☐
MULTIVITAMIN ☐

ALSO REMEMBER: Watch your intake of sodium, added sugar, alcohol

EAT WEIGHT WATCHERS POWER FOODS

FRUITS & VEGGIES ☐ ☐ ☐ ☐ ☐ ☐ ☐ ☐ ☐
NON-FAT & LOW-FAT DAIRY ☐ ☐ ☐
WHOLE GRAINS   LEAN PROTEINS

Non-fat dairy options are Power Foods and better for weight loss.

Day 3

	PointsPlus® value		POWER FOODS ▲
	+/−	balance	
My daily **PointsPlus** Target:			
My remaining daily **PointsPlus** Target total:			▲
Activity **PointsPlus** values earned:			
Activity **PointsPlus** values used:			
Weekly **PointsPlus** Allowance used:			

My Activity Today:	Duration

GOOD HEALTH GUIDELINES _____

HAVE DAILY: LIQUIDS ☐ ☐ ☐ ☐ ☐ ☐
HEALTHY OILS ☐ ☐
MULTIVITAMIN ☐

ALSO REMEMBER: Watch your intake of sodium, added sugar, alcohol

EAT WEIGHT WATCHERS POWER FOODS _____

FRUITS & VEGGIES ☐ ☐ ☐ ☐ ☐ ☐ ☐ ☐ ☐
NON-FAT & LOW-FAT DAIRY ☐ ☐ ☐
WHOLE GRAINS   LEAN PROTEINS

Non-fat dairy options are Power Foods and better for weight loss.

Day 4

	PointsPlus® value		POWER FOODS
	+/−	balance	▲
My daily **PointsPlus** Target:			
My remaining daily **PointsPlus** Target total:			▲
Activity **PointsPlus** values earned:			
Activity **PointsPlus** values used:			
Weekly **PointsPlus** Allowance used:			

My Activity Today:	Duration

GOOD HEALTH GUIDELINES

HAVE DAILY: LIQUIDS ☐ ☐ ☐ ☐ ☐ ☐
HEALTHY OILS ☐ ☐
MULTIVITAMIN ☐

ALSO REMEMBER: Watch your intake of sodium, added sugar, alcohol

EAT WEIGHT WATCHERS POWER FOODS

FRUITS & VEGGIES ☐ ☐ ☐ ☐ ☐ ☐ ☐ ☐ ☐
NON-FAT & LOW-FAT DAIRY ☐ ☐ ☐
WHOLE GRAINS   LEAN PROTEINS

Non-fat dairy options are Power Foods and better for weight loss.

Day 5

	PointsPlus® value		POWER FOODS ▲
	+/–	balance	
My daily *PointsPlus* Target:			
My remaining daily *PointsPlus* Target total:			▲
Activity *PointsPlus* values earned:			
Activity *PointsPlus* values used:			
Weekly *PointsPlus* Allowance used:			
My Activity Today:		Duration	

GOOD HEALTH GUIDELINES

HAVE DAILY: LIQUIDS ☐ ☐ ☐ ☐ ☐ ☐
HEALTHY OILS ☐ ☐
MULTIVITAMIN ☐

ALSO REMEMBER: Watch your intake of sodium, added sugar, alcohol

EAT WEIGHT WATCHERS POWER FOODS

FRUITS & VEGGIES ☐ ☐ ☐ ☐ ☐ ☐ ☐ ☐ ☐
NON-FAT & LOW-FAT DAIRY ☐ ☐ ☐
WHOLE GRAINS   LEAN PROTEINS

Non-fat dairy options are Power Foods and better for weight loss.

Day 6

	PointsPlus® value		POWER FOODS
	+/−	balance	▲
My daily PointsPlus Target:			
My remaining daily PointsPlus Target total:			▲
Activity PointsPlus values earned:			
Activity PointsPlus values used:			
Weekly PointsPlus Allowance used:			

My Activity Today:	Duration

GOOD HEALTH GUIDELINES

HAVE DAILY:
LIQUIDS ☐ ☐ ☐ ☐ ☐ ☐
HEALTHY OILS ☐ ☐
MULTIVITAMIN ☐

ALSO REMEMBER: Watch your intake of sodium, added sugar, alcohol

EAT WEIGHT WATCHERS POWER FOODS

FRUITS & VEGGIES ☐ ☐ ☐ ☐ ☐ ☐ ☐ ☐ ☐
NON-FAT & LOW-FAT DAIRY ☐ ☐ ☐
WHOLE GRAINS   LEAN PROTEINS

Non-fat dairy options are Power Foods and better for weight loss.

	PointsPlus® value		POWER FOODS ▲
	+/−	balance	
My daily *PointsPlus* Target:			
My remaining daily *PointsPlus* Target total:			▲
Activity *PointsPlus* values earned:			
Activity *PointsPlus* values used:			
Weekly *PointsPlus* Allowance used:			

My Activity Today:	Duration

GOOD HEALTH GUIDELINES

HAVE DAILY: LIQUIDS ☐ ☐ ☐ ☐ ☐ ☐
HEALTHY OILS ☐ ☐
MULTIVITAMIN ☐

ALSO REMEMBER: Watch your intake of sodium, added sugar, alcohol

EAT WEIGHT WATCHERS POWER FOODS

FRUITS & VEGGIES ☐ ☐ ☐ ☐ ☐ ☐ ☐ ☐ ☐
NON-FAT & LOW-FAT DAIRY ☐ ☐ ☐
WHOLE GRAINS   LEAN PROTEINS

Non-fat dairy options are Power Foods and better for weight loss.

Weekly Wrap-up

This week I lost/gained: _____

Meeting notes:

_____

_____

_____

_____

This week I learned:

_____

_____

_____

My Weekly *PointsPlus*® Allowance

49 48 47 46 45 44 43 42 41 40 39 38 37 36 35 34 33 32 31 30

29 28 27 26 25 24 23 22 21 20 19 18 17 16 15 14 13 12 11 10

9 8 7 6 5 4 3 2 1

My Weekly Activity *PointsPlus* Values

EARNED	1	2	3	4	5	6	7	8	9	10	11	12	13	14
USED	1	2	3	4	5	6	7	8	9	10	11	12	13	14
EARNED	15	16	17	18	19	20	21	22	23	24	25	26	27	28
USED	15	16	17	18	19	20	21	22	23	24	25	26	27	28
EARNED	29	30	31	32	33	34	35	36	37	38	39	40	41	42
USED	29	30	31	32	33	34	35	36	37	38	39	40	41	42

My Week at a Glance

	Day 1	Day 2	Day 3
What's coming this week			
Breakfast			
Lunch			
Dinner			
Snacks			
My Activity Plan			
Weekly *PointsPlus®* Allowance Allotted			

Date: _____ / _____ / _____

Day 4	Day 5	Day 6	Day 7

My Weekly To Do List

notes

Dishes to Make:

Name of Dish: _____
_____

Where to find it: _____
_____

Name of Dish: _____
_____

Where to find it: _____
_____

Name of Dish: _____
_____

Where to find it: _____
_____

Name of Dish: _____
_____

Where to find it: _____
_____

Name of Dish: _____
_____

Where to find it: _____
_____

Groceries:

_____	_____
_____	_____
_____	_____
_____	_____
_____	_____
_____	_____
_____	_____
_____	_____
_____	_____
_____	_____
_____	_____
_____	_____
_____	_____
_____	_____
_____	_____
_____	_____
_____	_____

tip Use the "Notes" pages in the back of this book to jot down recipes that worked well, and where to find them. You'll end up with a list of ideas for those days that you don't know what to make.

Date: /   /

Day 1

| | PointsPlus® value | | POWER FOODS ▲ |
	+/−	balance	
My daily **PointsPlus** Target:			
My remaining daily **PointsPlus** Target total:			▲
Activity **PointsPlus** values earned:			
Activity **PointsPlus** values used:			
Weekly **PointsPlus** Allowance used:			

My Activity Today:	Duration

GOOD HEALTH GUIDELINES

HAVE DAILY: LIQUIDS ☐ ☐ ☐ ☐ ☐ ☐
HEALTHY OILS ☐ ☐
MULTIVITAMIN ☐
ALSO REMEMBER: Watch your intake of sodium, added sugar, alcohol

EAT WEIGHT WATCHERS POWER FOODS

FRUITS & VEGGIES ☐ ☐ ☐ ☐ ☐ ☐ ☐ ☐
NON-FAT & LOW-FAT DAIRY ☐ ☐ ☐
WHOLE GRAINS   LEAN PROTEINS
Non-fat dairy options are Power Foods and better for weight loss.

Day 2

Date: /   /

| | PointsPlus® value | | POWER FOODS |
	+/–	balance	▲
My daily *PointsPlus* Target:			
My remaining daily *PointsPlus* Target total:			▲
Activity *PointsPlus* values earned:			
Activity *PointsPlus* values used:			
Weekly *PointsPlus* Allowance used:			

My Activity Today:	Duration

GOOD HEALTH GUIDELINES

HAVE DAILY: **LIQUIDS** ☐ ☐ ☐ ☐ ☐ ☐
               HEALTHY OILS ☐ ☐
               MULTIVITAMIN ☐

ALSO REMEMBER: Watch your intake of sodium, added sugar, alcohol

EAT WEIGHT WATCHERS POWER FOODS

FRUITS & VEGGIES ☐ ☐ ☐ ☐ ☐ ☐ ☐ ☐ ☐
NON-FAT & LOW-FAT DAIRY ☐ ☐ ☐
WHOLE GRAINS   LEAN PROTEINS

Non-fat dairy options are Power Foods and better for weight loss.

Day 3

	PointsPlus® value		POWER FOODS ▲
	+/−	balance	
My daily *PointsPlus* Target:			
My remaining daily *PointsPlus* Target total:			▲
Activity *PointsPlus* values earned:			
Activity *PointsPlus* values used:			
Weekly *PointsPlus* Allowance used:			

My Activity Today:	Duration

GOOD HEALTH GUIDELINES

HAVE DAILY: LIQUIDS ☐ ☐ ☐ ☐ ☐ ☐
HEALTHY OILS ☐ ☐
MULTIVITAMIN ☐

ALSO REMEMBER: Watch your intake of sodium, added sugar, alcohol

EAT WEIGHT WATCHERS POWER FOODS

FRUITS & VEGGIES ☐ ☐ ☐ ☐ ☐ ☐ ☐ ☐ ☐
NON-FAT & LOW-FAT DAIRY ☐ ☐ ☐
WHOLE GRAINS   LEAN PROTEINS

Non-fat dairy options are Power Foods and better for weight loss.

Day 4

Date: ___ / ___ / ___

	PointsPlus® value		POWER FOODS ▲
	+/−	balance	
My daily **PointsPlus** Target:			
My remaining daily **PointsPlus** Target total:			▲
Activity **PointsPlus** values earned:			
Activity **PointsPlus** values used:			
Weekly **PointsPlus** Allowance used:			

My Activity Today:	Duration

GOOD HEALTH GUIDELINES

HAVE DAILY: LIQUIDS ☐ ☐ ☐ ☐ ☐ ☐
HEALTHY OILS ☐ ☐
MULTIVITAMIN ☐

ALSO REMEMBER: Watch your intake of sodium, added sugar, alcohol

EAT WEIGHT WATCHERS POWER FOODS

FRUITS & VEGGIES ☐ ☐ ☐ ☐ ☐ ☐ ☐ ☐
NON-FAT & LOW-FAT DAIRY ☐ ☐ ☐
WHOLE GRAINS   LEAN PROTEINS

Non-fat dairy options are Power Foods and better for weight loss.

Day 5

| | *PointsPlus* value | | POWER FOODS |
	+/−	balance	▲
My daily *PointsPlus* Target:			
My remaining daily *PointsPlus* Target total:			▲
Activity *PointsPlus* values earned:			
Activity *PointsPlus* values used:			
Weekly *PointsPlus* Allowance used:			

My Activity Today:	Duration

GOOD HEALTH GUIDELINES

HAVE DAILY: LIQUIDS ☐ ☐ ☐ ☐ ☐ ☐
HEALTHY OILS ☐ ☐
MULTIVITAMIN ☐

ALSO REMEMBER: Watch your intake of sodium, added sugar, alcohol

EAT WEIGHT WATCHERS POWER FOODS

FRUITS & VEGGIES ☐ ☐ ☐ ☐ ☐ ☐ ☐ ☐ ☐
NON-FAT & LOW-FAT DAIRY ☐ ☐ ☐
WHOLE GRAINS   LEAN PROTEINS

Non-fat dairy options are Power Foods and better for weight loss.

Day 6

Date: _____ / _____ / _____

	PointsPlus® value		POWER FOODS
	+/–	balance	▲
My daily **PointsPlus** Target:			
My remaining daily **PointsPlus** Target total:			▲
Activity **PointsPlus** values earned:			
Activity **PointsPlus** values used:			
Weekly **PointsPlus** Allowance used:			

My Activity Today:	Duration

GOOD HEALTH GUIDELINES

HAVE DAILY: LIQUIDS ☐ ☐ ☐ ☐ ☐ ☐
　　　　　　 HEALTHY OILS ☐ ☐
　　　　　　 MULTIVITAMIN ☐

ALSO REMEMBER: Watch your intake of sodium, added sugar, alcohol

EAT WEIGHT WATCHERS POWER FOODS

FRUITS & VEGGIES ☐ ☐ ☐ ☐ ☐ ☐ ☐ ☐ ☐
NON-FAT & LOW-FAT DAIRY ☐ ☐ ☐
WHOLE GRAINS　LEAN PROTEINS

Non-fat dairy options are Power Foods and better for weight loss.

Day 7

	PointsPlus® value		POWER FOODS ▲
	+/−	balance	
My daily **PointsPlus** Target:			
My remaining daily **PointsPlus** Target total:			▲
Activity **PointsPlus** values earned:			
Activity **PointsPlus** values used:			
Weekly **PointsPlus** Allowance used:			

My Activity Today:	Duration

GOOD HEALTH GUIDELINES

HAVE DAILY: LIQUIDS ☐ ☐ ☐ ☐ ☐ ☐
　　　　　　HEALTHY OILS ☐ ☐
　　　　　　MULTIVITAMIN ☐

ALSO REMEMBER: Watch your intake of sodium, added sugar, alcohol

EAT WEIGHT WATCHERS POWER FOODS

FRUITS & VEGGIES ☐ ☐ ☐ ☐ ☐ ☐ ☐ ☐ ☐
NON-FAT & LOW-FAT DAIRY ☐ ☐ ☐
WHOLE GRAINS   LEAN PROTEINS

Non-fat dairy options are Power Foods and better for weight loss.

Weekly Wrap-up

This week I lost/gained: _____

Meeting notes:

_____

_____

_____

_____

This week I learned:

_____

_____

_____

My Weekly *PointsPlus®* Allowance

49 48 47 46 45 44 43 42 41 40 39 38 37 36 35 34 33 32 31 30

29 28 27 26 25 24 23 22 21 20 19 18 17 16 15 14 13 12 11 10

9 8 7 6 5 4 3 2 1

My Weekly Activity *PointsPlus* Values

EARNED	1	2	3	4	5	6	7	8	9	10	11	12	13	14
USED	1	2	3	4	5	6	7	8	9	10	11	12	13	14
EARNED	15	16	17	18	19	20	21	22	23	24	25	26	27	28
USED	15	16	17	18	19	20	21	22	23	24	25	26	27	28
EARNED	29	30	31	32	33	34	35	36	37	38	39	40	41	42
USED	29	30	31	32	33	34	35	36	37	38	39	40	41	42

My Week at a Glance

	Day 1	Day 2	Day 3
What's coming this week			
Breakfast			
Lunch			
Dinner			
Snacks			
My Activity Plan			
Weekly _PointsPlus®_ Allowance Allotted			

Date: / /

Day 4	Day 5	Day 6	Day 7

My Weekly To Do List

notes

Dishes to Make:

Name of Dish: _____

_____

Where to find it: _____

_____

Name of Dish: _____

_____

Where to find it: _____

_____

Name of Dish: _____

_____

Where to find it: _____

_____

Name of Dish: _____

_____

Where to find it: _____

_____

Name of Dish: _____

_____

Where to find it: _____

_____

Groceries:

_____   _____
_____   _____
_____   _____
_____   _____
_____   _____
_____   _____
_____   _____
_____   _____
_____   _____
_____   _____
_____   _____
_____   _____
_____   _____
_____   _____
_____   _____
_____   _____

tip Keeping containers of pre-rinsed and pre-cut fruits and vegetables in your refrigerator will increase your chances of grabbing them in a pinch, rather than having something less nutritious.

Day 1

	PointsPlus® value		POWER FOODS ▲
	+/–	balance	
My daily *PointsPlus* Target:			
My remaining daily *PointsPlus* Target total:			▲
Activity *PointsPlus* values earned:			
Activity *PointsPlus* values used:			
Weekly *PointsPlus* Allowance used:			

My Activity Today:	Duration

GOOD HEALTH GUIDELINES

HAVE DAILY: LIQUIDS ☐ ☐ ☐ ☐ ☐ ☐
HEALTHY OILS ☐ ☐
MULTIVITAMIN ☐

ALSO REMEMBER: Watch your intake of sodium, added sugar, alcohol

EAT WEIGHT WATCHERS POWER FOODS

FRUITS & VEGGIES ☐ ☐ ☐ ☐ ☐ ☐ ☐ ☐ ☐
NON-FAT & LOW-FAT DAIRY ☐ ☐ ☐
WHOLE GRAINS   LEAN PROTEINS

Non-fat dairy options are Power Foods and better for weight loss.

Day 2

| | PointsPlus® value | | POWER FOODS ▲ |
	+/−	balance	
My daily PointsPlus Target:			
My remaining daily PointsPlus Target total:			▲
Activity PointsPlus values earned:			
Activity PointsPlus values used:			
Weekly PointsPlus Allowance used:			
My Activity Today:		Duration	

GOOD HEALTH GUIDELINES

HAVE DAILY: LIQUIDS ☐ ☐ ☐ ☐ ☐ ☐
HEALTHY OILS ☐ ☐
MULTIVITAMIN ☐

ALSO REMEMBER: Watch your intake of sodium, added sugar, alcohol

EAT WEIGHT WATCHERS POWER FOODS

FRUITS & VEGGIES ☐ ☐ ☐ ☐ ☐ ☐ ☐ ☐ ☐
NON-FAT & LOW-FAT DAIRY ☐ ☐ ☐
WHOLE GRAINS   LEAN PROTEINS

Non-fat dairy options are Power Foods and better for weight loss.

	PointsPlus® value		POWER FOODS ▲
	+/−	balance	
My daily *PointsPlus* Target:			
My remaining daily *PointsPlus* Target total:			▲
Activity *PointsPlus* values earned:			
Activity *PointsPlus* values used:			
Weekly *PointsPlus* Allowance used:			
My Activity Today:		Duration	

GOOD HEALTH GUIDELINES

HAVE DAILY: LIQUIDS ☐ ☐ ☐ ☐ ☐ ☐
HEALTHY OILS ☐ ☐
MULTIVITAMIN ☐

ALSO REMEMBER: Watch your intake of sodium, added sugar, alcohol

EAT WEIGHT WATCHERS POWER FOODS

FRUITS & VEGGIES ☐ ☐ ☐ ☐ ☐ ☐ ☐ ☐ ☐
NON-FAT & LOW-FAT DAIRY ☐ ☐ ☐
WHOLE GRAINS   LEAN PROTEINS

Non-fat dairy options are Power Foods and better for weight loss.

Day 4

| | PointsPlus® value | | POWER FOODS ▲ |
	+/–	balance	
My daily **PointsPlus** Target:			
My remaining daily **PointsPlus** Target total:			▲
Activity **PointsPlus** values earned:			
Activity **PointsPlus** values used:			
Weekly **PointsPlus** Allowance used:			
My Activity Today:		Duration	

GOOD HEALTH GUIDELINES

HAVE DAILY: LIQUIDS ☐ ☐ ☐ ☐ ☐ ☐
HEALTHY OILS ☐ ☐
MULTIVITAMIN ☐

ALSO REMEMBER: Watch your intake of sodium, added sugar, alcohol

EAT WEIGHT WATCHERS POWER FOODS

FRUITS & VEGGIES ☐ ☐ ☐ ☐ ☐ ☐ ☐ ☐
NON-FAT & LOW-FAT DAIRY ☐ ☐ ☐
WHOLE GRAINS   LEAN PROTEINS

Non-fat dairy options are Power Foods and better for weight loss.

	PointsPlus® value		POWER FOODS ▲
	+/−	balance	
My daily **PointsPlus** Target:			
My remaining daily **PointsPlus** Target total:			▲
Activity **PointsPlus** values earned:			
Activity **PointsPlus** values used:			
Weekly **PointsPlus** Allowance used:			

My Activity Today:	Duration

GOOD HEALTH GUIDELINES

HAVE DAILY: LIQUIDS ☐☐☐☐☐☐
HEALTHY OILS ☐☐
MULTIVITAMIN ☐

ALSO REMEMBER: Watch your intake of sodium, added sugar, alcohol

EAT WEIGHT WATCHERS POWER FOODS

FRUITS & VEGGIES ☐☐☐☐☐☐☐☐☐
NON-FAT & LOW-FAT DAIRY ☐☐☐
WHOLE GRAINS   LEAN PROTEINS

Non-fat dairy options are Power Foods and better for weight loss.

Day 6

Date: /   /

	PointsPlus® value		POWER FOODS
	+/−	balance	▲
My daily PointsPlus Target:			
My remaining daily PointsPlus Target total:			▲
Activity PointsPlus values earned:			
Activity PointsPlus values used:			
Weekly PointsPlus Allowance used:			

My Activity Today:	Duration

GOOD HEALTH GUIDELINES

HAVE DAILY: LIQUIDS ☐☐☐☐☐☐
HEALTHY OILS ☐☐
MULTIVITAMIN ☐

ALSO REMEMBER: Watch your intake of sodium, added sugar, alcohol

EAT WEIGHT WATCHERS POWER FOODS

FRUITS & VEGGIES ☐☐☐☐☐☐☐☐☐
NON-FAT & LOW-FAT DAIRY ☐☐☐
WHOLE GRAINS   LEAN PROTEINS

Non-fat dairy options are Power Foods and better for weight loss.

Day 7

	PointsPlus® value		POWER FOODS ▲
	+/−	balance	
My daily PointsPlus Target:			
My remaining daily PointsPlus Target total:			▲
Activity PointsPlus values earned:			
Activity PointsPlus values used:			
Weekly PointsPlus Allowance used:			
My Activity Today:		Duration	

GOOD HEALTH GUIDELINES

HAVE DAILY: LIQUIDS ☐☐☐☐☐☐
HEALTHY OILS ☐☐
MULTIVITAMIN ☐

ALSO REMEMBER: Watch your intake of sodium, added sugar, alcohol

EAT WEIGHT WATCHERS POWER FOODS

FRUITS & VEGGIES ☐☐☐☐☐☐☐☐☐
NON-FAT & LOW-FAT DAIRY ☐☐☐
WHOLE GRAINS   LEAN PROTEINS

Non-fat dairy options are Power Foods and better for weight loss.

Weekly Wrap-up

This week I lost/gained: _____

Meeting notes:

_____

_____

_____

_____

This week I learned:

_____

_____

_____

My Weekly *PointsPlus*® Allowance

49 48 47 46 45 44 43 42 41 40 39 38 37 36 35 34 33 32 31 30

29 28 27 26 25 24 23 22 21 20 19 18 17 16 15 14 13 12 11 10

9 8 7 6 5 4 3 2 1

My Weekly Activity *PointsPlus* Values

EARNED	1	2	3	4	5	6	7	8	9	10	11	12	13	14
USED	1	2	3	4	5	6	7	8	9	10	11	12	13	14
EARNED	15	16	17	18	19	20	21	22	23	24	25	26	27	28
USED	15	16	17	18	19	20	21	22	23	24	25	26	27	28
EARNED	29	30	31	32	33	34	35	36	37	38	39	40	41	42
USED	29	30	31	32	33	34	35	36	37	38	39	40	41	42

6 My Week at a Glance

	Day 1	Day 2	Day 3
What's coming this week			
Breakfast			
Lunch			
Dinner			
Snacks			
My Activity Plan			
Weekly *PointsPlus*® Allowance Allotted			

Date: /   /

Day 4	Day 5	Day 6	Day 7

My Weekly To Do List

notes

Dishes to Make:

Name of Dish: _____
_____

Where to find it: _____
_____

Name of Dish: _____
_____

Where to find it: _____
_____

Name of Dish: _____
_____

Where to find it: _____
_____

Name of Dish: _____
_____

Where to find it: _____
_____

Name of Dish: _____
_____

Where to find it: _____
_____

Groceries:

_____   _____
_____   _____
_____   _____
_____   _____
_____   _____
_____   _____
_____   _____
_____   _____
_____   _____
_____   _____
_____   _____
_____   _____
_____   _____
_____   _____
_____   _____
_____   _____
_____   _____

tip What is "stressed" spelled backward? Coincidence?
You decide.

	PointsPlus® value		POWER FOODS ▲
	+/−	balance	
My daily **PointsPlus** Target:			
My remaining daily **PointsPlus** Target total:			▲
Activity **PointsPlus** values earned:			
Activity **PointsPlus** values used:			
Weekly **PointsPlus** Allowance used:			
My Activity Today:		Duration	

GOOD HEALTH GUIDELINES

HAVE DAILY: LIQUIDS ☐☐☐☐☐☐
HEALTHY OILS ☐☐
MULTIVITAMIN ☐

ALSO REMEMBER: Watch your intake of sodium, added sugar, alcohol

EAT WEIGHT WATCHERS POWER FOODS

FRUITS & VEGGIES ☐☐☐☐☐☐☐☐☐
NON-FAT & LOW-FAT DAIRY ☐☐☐
WHOLE GRAINS   LEAN PROTEINS

Non-fat dairy options are Power Foods and better for weight loss.

| | PointsPlus® value | | POWER FOODS |
	+/-	balance	▲
My daily PointsPlus Target:			
My remaining daily PointsPlus Target total:			▲
Activity PointsPlus values earned:			
Activity PointsPlus values used:			
Weekly PointsPlus Allowance used:			
My Activity Today:		Duration	

GOOD HEALTH GUIDELINES

HAVE DAILY: LIQUIDS ☐ ☐ ☐ ☐ ☐ ☐
HEALTHY OILS ☐ ☐
MULTIVITAMIN ☐

ALSO REMEMBER: Watch your intake of sodium, added sugar, alcohol

EAT WEIGHT WATCHERS POWER FOODS

FRUITS & VEGGIES ☐ ☐ ☐ ☐ ☐ ☐ ☐ ☐ ☐
NON-FAT & LOW-FAT DAIRY ☐ ☐ ☐
WHOLE GRAINS   LEAN PROTEINS

Non-fat dairy options are Power Foods and better for weight loss.

	PointsPlus® value		POWER FOODS ▲
	+/-	balance	
My daily *PointsPlus* Target:			
My remaining daily *PointsPlus* Target total:			▲
Activity *PointsPlus* values earned:			
Activity *PointsPlus* values used:			
Weekly *PointsPlus* Allowance used:			
My Activity Today:		Duration	

GOOD HEALTH GUIDELINES

HAVE DAILY: LIQUIDS ☐ ☐ ☐ ☐ ☐ ☐
HEALTHY OILS ☐ ☐
MULTIVITAMIN ☐

ALSO REMEMBER: Watch your intake of sodium, added sugar, alcohol

EAT WEIGHT WATCHERS POWER FOODS

FRUITS & VEGGIES ☐ ☐ ☐ ☐ ☐ ☐ ☐ ☐ ☐
NON-FAT & LOW-FAT DAIRY ☐ ☐ ☐
WHOLE GRAINS   LEAN PROTEINS
Non-fat dairy options are Power Foods and better for weight loss.

Day 4

	PointsPlus® value		POWER FOODS
	+/−	balance	▲
My daily **PointsPlus** Target:			
My remaining daily **PointsPlus** Target total:			▲
Activity **PointsPlus** values earned:			
Activity **PointsPlus** values used:			
Weekly **PointsPlus** Allowance used:			
My Activity Today:		Duration	

GOOD HEALTH GUIDELINES

HAVE DAILY: LIQUIDS ☐ ☐ ☐ ☐ ☐ ☐
HEALTHY OILS ☐ ☐
MULTIVITAMIN ☐

ALSO REMEMBER: Watch your intake of sodium, added sugar, alcohol

EAT WEIGHT WATCHERS POWER FOODS

FRUITS & VEGGIES ☐ ☐ ☐ ☐ ☐ ☐ ☐ ☐ ☐
NON-FAT & LOW-FAT DAIRY ☐ ☐ ☐
WHOLE GRAINS   LEAN PROTEINS

Non-fat dairy options are Power Foods and better for weight loss.

Date: / /

Day 5

	PointsPlus® value		POWER FOODS ▲
	+/−	balance	
My daily **PointsPlus** Target:			
My remaining daily **PointsPlus** Target total:			▲
Activity **PointsPlus** values earned:			
Activity **PointsPlus** values used:			
Weekly **PointsPlus** Allowance used:			

My Activity Today:	Duration

GOOD HEALTH GUIDELINES

HAVE DAILY: LIQUIDS ☐ ☐ ☐ ☐ ☐ ☐
HEALTHY OILS ☐ ☐
MULTIVITAMIN ☐

ALSO REMEMBER: Watch your intake of sodium, added sugar, alcohol

EAT WEIGHT WATCHERS POWER FOODS

FRUITS & VEGGIES ☐ ☐ ☐ ☐ ☐ ☐ ☐ ☐
NON-FAT & LOW-FAT DAIRY ☐ ☐ ☐
WHOLE GRAINS   LEAN PROTEINS

Non-fat dairy options are Power Foods and better for weight loss.

Day 6

Date: /   /

	PointsPlus® value		POWER FOODS ▲
	+/−	balance	
My daily *PointsPlus* Target:			
My remaining daily *PointsPlus* Target total:			▲
Activity *PointsPlus* values earned:			
Activity *PointsPlus* values used:			
Weekly *PointsPlus* Allowance used:			

My Activity Today:	Duration

GOOD HEALTH GUIDELINES

HAVE DAILY: LIQUIDS ☐ ☐ ☐ ☐ ☐ ☐
                HEALTHY OILS ☐ ☐
                MULTIVITAMIN ☐

ALSO REMEMBER: Watch your intake of sodium, added sugar, alcohol

EAT WEIGHT WATCHERS POWER FOODS

FRUITS & VEGGIES ☐ ☐ ☐ ☐ ☐ ☐ ☐ ☐ ☐
NON-FAT & LOW-FAT DAIRY ☐ ☐ ☐
WHOLE GRAINS   LEAN PROTEINS

Non-fat dairy options are Power Foods and better for weight loss.

	PointsPlus® value		POWER FOODS ▲
	+/−	balance	
My daily *PointsPlus* Target:			
My remaining daily *PointsPlus* Target total:			▲
Activity *PointsPlus* values earned:			
Activity *PointsPlus* values used:			
Weekly *PointsPlus* Allowance used:			
My Activity Today:		Duration	

GOOD HEALTH GUIDELINES

HAVE DAILY: LIQUIDS ☐ ☐ ☐ ☐ ☐ ☐
HEALTHY OILS ☐ ☐
MULTIVITAMIN ☐

ALSO REMEMBER: Watch your intake of sodium, added sugar, alcohol

EAT WEIGHT WATCHERS POWER FOODS

FRUITS & VEGGIES ☐ ☐ ☐ ☐ ☐ ☐ ☐ ☐ ☐
NON-FAT & LOW-FAT DAIRY ☐ ☐ ☐
WHOLE GRAINS   LEAN PROTEINS

Non-fat dairy options are Power Foods and better for weight loss.

Weekly Wrap-up

This week I lost/gained: _____

Meeting notes:

_____

_____

_____

_____

This week I learned:

_____

_____

_____

My Weekly *PointsPlus*® Allowance

49 48 47 46 45 44 43 42 41 40 39 38 37 36 35 34 33 32 31 30

29 28 27 26 25 24 23 22 21 20 19 18 17 16 15 14 13 12 11 10

9 8 7 6 5 4 3 2 1

My Weekly Activity *PointsPlus* Values

EARNED	1	2	3	4	5	6	7	8	9	10	11	12	13	14
USED	1	2	3	4	5	6	7	8	9	10	11	12	13	14
EARNED	15	16	17	18	19	20	21	22	23	24	25	26	27	28
USED	15	16	17	18	19	20	21	22	23	24	25	26	27	28
EARNED	29	30	31	32	33	34	35	36	37	38	39	40	41	42
USED	29	30	31	32	33	34	35	36	37	38	39	40	41	42

My Week at a Glance

	Day 1	Day 2	Day 3
What's coming this week			
Breakfast			
Lunch			
Dinner			
Snacks			
My Activity Plan			
Weekly *PointsPlus*® Allowance Allotted			

Date: /   /

Day 4	Day 5	Day 6	Day 7

My Weekly To Do List

notes

Dishes to Make:

Name of Dish: _____

_____

Where to find it: _____

_____

Name of Dish: _____

_____

Where to find it: _____

_____

Name of Dish: _____

_____

Where to find it: _____

_____

Name of Dish: _____

_____

Where to find it: _____

_____

Name of Dish: _____

_____

Where to find it: _____

_____

Groceries:

_____   _____
_____   _____
_____   _____
_____   _____
_____   _____
_____   _____
_____   _____
_____   _____
_____   _____
_____   _____
_____   _____
_____   _____
_____   _____
_____   _____
_____   _____
_____   _____
_____   _____
_____   _____

tip   Stash nutritious shelf-stable foods wherever possible—
in your car, in your desk, in your handbag—for those
days that you barely have time to take a bathroom
break, much less time to prepare a meal.

Day 1

	PointsPlus® value		POWER FOODS ▲
	+/−	balance	
My daily *PointsPlus* Target:			
My remaining daily *PointsPlus* Target total:			▲
Activity *PointsPlus* values earned:			
Activity *PointsPlus* values used:			
Weekly *PointsPlus* Allowance used:			
My Activity Today:		Duration	

GOOD HEALTH GUIDELINES

HAVE DAILY: LIQUIDS ☐☐☐☐☐☐
HEALTHY OILS ☐☐
MULTIVITAMIN ☐

ALSO REMEMBER: Watch your intake of sodium, added sugar, alcohol

EAT WEIGHT WATCHERS POWER FOODS

FRUITS & VEGGIES ☐☐☐☐☐☐☐☐☐
NON-FAT & LOW-FAT DAIRY ☐☐☐
WHOLE GRAINS   LEAN PROTEINS
Non-fat dairy options are Power Foods and better for weight loss.

Day 2

Date: /   /

	PointsPlus® value		POWER FOODS ▲
	+/−	balance	
My daily PointsPlus Target:			
My remaining daily PointsPlus Target total:			▲
Activity PointsPlus values earned:			
Activity PointsPlus values used:			
Weekly PointsPlus Allowance used:			
My Activity Today:		Duration	

GOOD HEALTH GUIDELINES

HAVE DAILY: LIQUIDS ☐ ☐ ☐ ☐ ☐ ☐
             HEALTHY OILS ☐ ☐
             MULTIVITAMIN ☐

ALSO REMEMBER: Watch your intake of sodium, added sugar, alcohol

EAT WEIGHT WATCHERS POWER FOODS

FRUITS & VEGGIES ☐ ☐ ☐ ☐ ☐ ☐ ☐ ☐ ☐
NON-FAT & LOW-FAT DAIRY ☐ ☐ ☐
WHOLE GRAINS   LEAN PROTEINS

Non-fat dairy options are Power Foods and better for weight loss.

Day 3

	PointsPlus® value		POWER FOODS ▲
	+/−	balance	
My daily **PointsPlus** Target:			
My remaining daily **PointsPlus** Target total:			▲
Activity **PointsPlus** values earned:			
Activity **PointsPlus** values used:			
Weekly **PointsPlus** Allowance used:			
My Activity Today:		Duration	

GOOD HEALTH GUIDELINES

HAVE DAILY: LIQUIDS ☐☐☐☐☐☐
HEALTHY OILS ☐☐
MULTIVITAMIN ☐

ALSO REMEMBER: Watch your intake of sodium, added sugar, alcohol

EAT WEIGHT WATCHERS POWER FOODS

FRUITS & VEGGIES ☐☐☐☐☐☐☐☐☐
NON-FAT & LOW-FAT DAIRY ☐☐☐
WHOLE GRAINS   LEAN PROTEINS

Non-fat dairy options are Power Foods and better for weight loss.

Day 4

Date: /   /

	PointsPlus® value		POWER FOODS ▲
	+/−	balance	
My daily *PointsPlus* Target:			
My remaining daily *PointsPlus* Target total:			▲
Activity *PointsPlus* values earned:			
Activity *PointsPlus* values used:			
Weekly *PointsPlus* Allowance used:			
My Activity Today:		Duration	

GOOD HEALTH GUIDELINES

HAVE DAILY: LIQUIDS ☐ ☐ ☐ ☐ ☐ ☐
HEALTHY OILS ☐ ☐
MULTIVITAMIN ☐

ALSO REMEMBER: Watch your intake of sodium, added sugar, alcohol

EAT WEIGHT WATCHERS POWER FOODS

FRUITS & VEGGIES ☐ ☐ ☐ ☐ ☐ ☐ ☐ ☐ ☐
NON-FAT & LOW-FAT DAIRY ☐ ☐ ☐
WHOLE GRAINS   LEAN PROTEINS

Non-fat dairy options are Power Foods and better for weight loss.

	PointsPlus® value		POWER FOODS ▲
	+/−	balance	
My daily *PointsPlus* Target:			
My remaining daily *PointsPlus* Target total:			
Activity *PointsPlus* values earned:			
Activity *PointsPlus* values used:			
Weekly *PointsPlus* Allowance used:			

My Activity Today:	Duration

Day 6

	PointsPlus® value		POWER FOODS ▲
	+/−	balance	
My daily PointsPlus Target:			
My remaining daily PointsPlus Target total:			▲
Activity PointsPlus values earned:			
Activity PointsPlus values used:			
Weekly PointsPlus Allowance used:			

My Activity Today:	Duration

GOOD HEALTH GUIDELINES

HAVE DAILY: LIQUIDS ☐ ☐ ☐ ☐ ☐ ☐
HEALTHY OILS ☐ ☐
MULTIVITAMIN ☐

ALSO REMEMBER: Watch your intake of sodium, added sugar, alcohol

EAT WEIGHT WATCHERS POWER FOODS

FRUITS & VEGGIES ☐ ☐ ☐ ☐ ☐ ☐ ☐ ☐ ☐
NON-FAT & LOW-FAT DAIRY ☐ ☐ ☐
WHOLE GRAINS LEAN PROTEINS

Non-fat dairy options are Power Foods and better for weight loss.

Day 7

	PointsPlus® value		POWER FOODS
	+/−	balance	▲
My daily *PointsPlus* Target:			
My remaining daily *PointsPlus* Target total:			▲
Activity *PointsPlus* values earned:			
Activity *PointsPlus* values used:			
Weekly *PointsPlus* Allowance used:			

My Activity Today:	Duration

GOOD HEALTH GUIDELINES

HAVE DAILY: LIQUIDS ☐ ☐ ☐ ☐ ☐ ☐
HEALTHY OILS ☐ ☐
MULTIVITAMIN ☐

ALSO REMEMBER: Watch your intake of sodium, added sugar, alcohol

EAT WEIGHT WATCHERS POWER FOODS

FRUITS & VEGGIES ☐ ☐ ☐ ☐ ☐ ☐ ☐ ☐ ☐
NON-FAT & LOW-FAT DAIRY ☐ ☐ ☐
WHOLE GRAINS   LEAN PROTEINS

Non-fat dairy options are Power Foods and better for weight loss.

Weekly Wrap-up

This week I lost/gained: _____

Meeting notes:

_____

_____

_____

_____

This week I learned:

_____

_____

_____

My Weekly *PointsPlus*® Allowance

49 48 47 46 45 44 43 42 41 40 39 38 37 36 35 34 33 32 31 30

29 28 27 26 25 24 23 22 21 20 19 18 17 16 15 14 13 12 11 10

9 8 7 6 5 4 3 2 1

My Weekly Activity *PointsPlus* Values

EARNED	1	2	3	4	5	6	7	8	9	10	11	12	13	14
USED	1	2	3	4	5	6	7	8	9	10	11	12	13	14
EARNED	15	16	17	18	19	20	21	22	23	24	25	26	27	28
USED	15	16	17	18	19	20	21	22	23	24	25	26	27	28
EARNED	29	30	31	32	33	34	35	36	37	38	39	40	41	42
USED	29	30	31	32	33	34	35	36	37	38	39	40	41	42

8 My Week at a Glance

	Day 1	Day 2	Day 3
What's coming this week			
Breakfast			
Lunch			
Dinner			
Snacks			
My Activity Plan			
Weekly *PointsPlus*® Allowance Allotted			

Date: _____ / _____ / _____

Day 4	Day 5	Day 6	Day 7

My Weekly To Do List

notes

Dishes to Make:

Name of Dish: _____
_____

Where to find it: _____
_____

Name of Dish: _____
_____

Where to find it: _____
_____

Name of Dish: _____
_____

Where to find it: _____
_____

Name of Dish: _____
_____

Where to find it: _____
_____

Name of Dish: _____
_____

Where to find it: _____
_____

Groceries:

_____ _____
_____ _____
_____ _____
_____ _____
_____ _____
_____ _____
_____ _____
_____ _____
_____ _____
_____ _____
_____ _____
_____ _____
_____ _____
_____ _____
_____ _____
_____ _____
_____ _____
_____ _____

tip When having fast food, order a small. Period.

Date: _____ / _____ / _____

Day 1

	PointsPlus® value		POWER FOODS ▲
	+/−	balance	
My daily **PointsPlus** Target:			
My remaining daily **PointsPlus** Target total:			▲
Activity **PointsPlus** values earned:			
Activity **PointsPlus** values used:			
Weekly **PointsPlus** Allowance used:			
My Activity Today:		Duration	

GOOD HEALTH GUIDELINES

HAVE DAILY: LIQUIDS ☐☐☐☐☐☐
HEALTHY OILS ☐☐
MULTIVITAMIN ☐

ALSO REMEMBER: Watch your intake of sodium, added sugar, alcohol

EAT WEIGHT WATCHERS POWER FOODS

FRUITS & VEGGIES ☐☐☐☐☐☐☐☐☐
NON-FAT & LOW-FAT DAIRY ☐☐☐
WHOLE GRAINS   LEAN PROTEINS

Non-fat dairy options are Power Foods and better for weight loss.

Day 2

	PointsPlus® value		POWER FOODS
	+/−	balance	▲
My daily **PointsPlus** Target:			
My remaining daily **PointsPlus** Target total:			▲
Activity **PointsPlus** values earned:			
Activity **PointsPlus** values used:			
Weekly **PointsPlus** Allowance used:			

My Activity Today:	Duration

GOOD HEALTH GUIDELINES

HAVE DAILY: LIQUIDS ☐ ☐ ☐ ☐ ☐ ☐
HEALTHY OILS ☐ ☐
MULTIVITAMIN ☐

ALSO REMEMBER: Watch your intake of sodium, added sugar, alcohol

EAT WEIGHT WATCHERS POWER FOODS

FRUITS & VEGGIES ☐ ☐ ☐ ☐ ☐ ☐ ☐ ☐ ☐
NON-FAT & LOW-FAT DAIRY ☐ ☐ ☐
WHOLE GRAINS   LEAN PROTEINS

Non-fat dairy options are Power Foods and better for weight loss.

Date: / /

Day 3

	PointsPlus® value		POWER FOODS
	+/−	balance	▲
My daily **PointsPlus** Target:			
My remaining daily **PointsPlus** Target total:			▲
Activity **PointsPlus** values earned:			
Activity **PointsPlus** values used:			
Weekly **PointsPlus** Allowance used:			

My Activity Today:	Duration

GOOD HEALTH GUIDELINES

HAVE DAILY: LIQUIDS ☐ ☐ ☐ ☐ ☐ ☐
HEALTHY OILS ☐ ☐
MULTIVITAMIN ☐

ALSO REMEMBER: Watch your intake of sodium, added sugar, alcohol

EAT WEIGHT WATCHERS POWER FOODS

FRUITS & VEGGIES ☐ ☐ ☐ ☐ ☐ ☐ ☐ ☐ ☐
NON-FAT & LOW-FAT DAIRY ☐ ☐ ☐
WHOLE GRAINS   LEAN PROTEINS

Non-fat dairy options are Power Foods and better for weight loss.

Day 4

	PointsPlus® value		POWER FOODS
	+/-	balance	▲
My daily **PointsPlus** Target:			
My remaining daily **PointsPlus** Target total:			▲
Activity **PointsPlus** values earned:			
Activity **PointsPlus** values used:			
Weekly **PointsPlus** Allowance used:			

My Activity Today:	Duration

GOOD HEALTH GUIDELINES

HAVE DAILY: LIQUIDS ☐ ☐ ☐ ☐ ☐ ☐
HEALTHY OILS ☐ ☐
MULTIVITAMIN ☐

ALSO REMEMBER: Watch your intake of sodium, added sugar, alcohol

EAT WEIGHT WATCHERS POWER FOODS

FRUITS & VEGGIES ☐ ☐ ☐ ☐ ☐ ☐ ☐ ☐
NON-FAT & LOW-FAT DAIRY ☐ ☐ ☐
WHOLE GRAINS   LEAN PROTEINS

Non-fat dairy options are Power Foods and better for weight loss.

Date: ___ / ___ / ___

Day 5

	PointsPlus® value		POWER FOODS ▲
	+/−	balance	
My daily **PointsPlus** Target:			
My remaining daily **PointsPlus** Target total:			▲
Activity **PointsPlus** values earned:			
Activity **PointsPlus** values used:			
Weekly **PointsPlus** Allowance used:			

My Activity Today:	Duration

GOOD HEALTH GUIDELINES

HAVE DAILY: LIQUIDS ☐ ☐ ☐ ☐ ☐ ☐
HEALTHY OILS ☐ ☐
MULTIVITAMIN ☐

ALSO REMEMBER: Watch your intake of sodium, added sugar, alcohol

EAT WEIGHT WATCHERS POWER FOODS

FRUITS & VEGGIES ☐ ☐ ☐ ☐ ☐ ☐ ☐ ☐ ☐
NON-FAT & LOW-FAT DAIRY ☐ ☐ ☐
WHOLE GRAINS   LEAN PROTEINS

Non-fat dairy options are Power Foods and better for weight loss.

Day 6

	PointsPlus® value		POWER FOODS
	+/−	balance	▲
My daily **PointsPlus** Target:			
My remaining daily **PointsPlus** Target total:			▲
Activity **PointsPlus** values earned:			
Activity **PointsPlus** values used:			
Weekly **PointsPlus** Allowance used:			

My Activity Today:	Duration

GOOD HEALTH GUIDELINES

HAVE DAILY: LIQUIDS ☐☐☐☐☐☐
HEALTHY OILS ☐☐
MULTIVITAMIN ☐

ALSO REMEMBER: Watch your intake of sodium, added sugar, alcohol

EAT WEIGHT WATCHERS POWER FOODS

FRUITS & VEGGIES ☐☐☐☐☐☐☐☐☐
NON-FAT & LOW-FAT DAIRY ☐☐☐
WHOLE GRAINS   LEAN PROTEINS

Non-fat dairy options are Power Foods and better for weight loss.

Day 7

	PointsPlus® value		POWER FOODS ▲
	+/−	balance	
My daily *PointsPlus* Target:			
My remaining daily *PointsPlus* Target total:			▲
Activity *PointsPlus* values earned:			
Activity *PointsPlus* values used:			
Weekly *PointsPlus* Allowance used:			
My Activity Today:		Duration	

GOOD HEALTH GUIDELINES

HAVE DAILY: LIQUIDS ☐ ☐ ☐ ☐ ☐ ☐
HEALTHY OILS ☐ ☐
MULTIVITAMIN ☐

ALSO REMEMBER: Watch your intake of sodium, added sugar, alcohol

EAT WEIGHT WATCHERS POWER FOODS

FRUITS & VEGGIES ☐ ☐ ☐ ☐ ☐ ☐ ☐ ☐ ☐
NON-FAT & LOW-FAT DAIRY ☐ ☐ ☐
WHOLE GRAINS   LEAN PROTEINS
Non-fat dairy options are Power Foods and better for weight loss.

Weekly Wrap-up

This week I lost/gained: _____

Meeting notes:

_____

_____

_____

_____

This week I learned:

_____

_____

_____

My Weekly *PointsPlus*® Allowance

49 48 47 46 45 44 43 42 41 40 39 38 37 36 35 34 33 32 31 30

29 28 27 26 25 24 23 22 21 20 19 18 17 16 15 14 13 12 11 10

9 8 7 6 5 4 3 2 1

My Weekly Activity *PointsPlus* Values

EARNED	1	2	3	4	5	6	7	8	9	10	11	12	13	14
USED	1	2	3	4	5	6	7	8	9	10	11	12	13	14
EARNED	15	16	17	18	19	20	21	22	23	24	25	26	27	28
USED	15	16	17	18	19	20	21	22	23	24	25	26	27	28
EARNED	29	30	31	32	33	34	35	36	37	38	39	40	41	42
USED	29	30	31	32	33	34	35	36	37	38	39	40	41	42

My Week at a Glance

	Day 1	Day 2	Day 3
What's coming this week			
Breakfast			
Lunch			
Dinner			
Snacks			
My Activity Plan			
Weekly *PointsPlus*® Allowance Allotted			

Date: /   /

Day 4	Day 5	Day 6	Day 7

My Weekly To Do List

notes

Dishes to Make:

Name of Dish: _____

_____

Where to find it: _____

_____

Name of Dish: _____

_____

Where to find it: _____

_____

Name of Dish: _____

_____

Where to find it: _____

_____

Name of Dish: _____

_____

Where to find it: _____

_____

Name of Dish: _____

_____

Where to find it: _____

_____

Groceries:

_____   _____
_____   _____
_____   _____
_____   _____
_____   _____
_____   _____
_____   _____
_____   _____
_____   _____
_____   _____
_____   _____
_____   _____
_____   _____
_____   _____
_____   _____
_____   _____
_____   _____
_____   _____

tip Have a black magic marker available when you're unpacking your groceries. Write the *PointsPlus* values on the outside of the packages before you put them away.

Date: ___/___/___

Day 1

	PointsPlus® value		POWER FOODS ▲
	+/−	balance	
My daily *PointsPlus* Target:			
My remaining daily *PointsPlus* Target total:			▲
Activity *PointsPlus* values earned:			
Activity *PointsPlus* values used:			
Weekly *PointsPlus* Allowance used:			
My Activity Today:		Duration	

GOOD HEALTH GUIDELINES

HAVE DAILY: LIQUIDS ☐☐☐☐☐☐
HEALTHY OILS ☐☐
MULTIVITAMIN ☐

ALSO REMEMBER: Watch your intake of sodium, added sugar, alcohol

EAT WEIGHT WATCHERS POWER FOODS

FRUITS & VEGGIES ☐☐☐☐☐☐☐☐☐
NON-FAT & LOW-FAT DAIRY ☐☐☐
WHOLE GRAINS   LEAN PROTEINS

Non-fat dairy options are Power Foods and better for weight loss.

Day 2

week

	PointsPlus® value		POWER FOODS
	+/−	balance	▲
My daily PointsPlus Target:			
My remaining daily PointsPlus Target total:			▲
Activity PointsPlus values earned:			
Activity PointsPlus values used:			
Weekly PointsPlus Allowance used:			

My Activity Today:	Duration

GOOD HEALTH GUIDELINES

HAVE DAILY: LIQUIDS ☐☐☐☐☐☐
HEALTHY OILS ☐☐
MULTIVITAMIN ☐

ALSO REMEMBER: Watch your intake of sodium, added sugar, alcohol

EAT WEIGHT WATCHERS POWER FOODS

FRUITS & VEGGIES ☐☐☐☐☐☐☐☐☐
NON-FAT & LOW-FAT DAIRY ☐☐☐
WHOLE GRAINS   LEAN PROTEINS
Non-fat dairy options are Power Foods and better for weight loss.

	PointsPlus® value		POWER FOODS ▲
	+/−	balance	
My daily *PointsPlus* Target:			
My remaining daily *PointsPlus* Target total:			▲
Activity *PointsPlus* values earned:			
Activity *PointsPlus* values used:			
Weekly *PointsPlus* Allowance used:			

My Activity Today:	Duration

GOOD HEALTH GUIDELINES _____

HAVE DAILY: LIQUIDS ☐ ☐ ☐ ☐ ☐ ☐
           HEALTHY OILS ☐ ☐
           MULTIVITAMIN ☐

ALSO REMEMBER: Watch your intake of sodium, added sugar, alcohol

EAT WEIGHT WATCHERS POWER FOODS _____

FRUITS & VEGGIES ☐ ☐ ☐ ☐ ☐ ☐ ☐ ☐ ☐
NON-FAT & LOW-FAT DAIRY ☐ ☐ ☐
WHOLE GRAINS   LEAN PROTEINS

Non-fat dairy options are Power Foods and better for weight loss.

Day 4

	PointsPlus® value		POWER FOODS ▲
	+/−	balance	
My daily PointsPlus Target:			
My remaining daily PointsPlus Target total:			▲
Activity PointsPlus values earned:			
Activity PointsPlus values used:			
Weekly PointsPlus Allowance used:			
My Activity Today:		Duration	

GOOD HEALTH GUIDELINES

HAVE DAILY: LIQUIDS ☐ ☐ ☐ ☐ ☐ ☐
HEALTHY OILS ☐ ☐
MULTIVITAMIN ☐
ALSO REMEMBER: Watch your intake of sodium, added sugar, alcohol

EAT WEIGHT WATCHERS POWER FOODS

FRUITS & VEGGIES ☐ ☐ ☐ ☐ ☐ ☐ ☐ ☐ ☐
NON-FAT & LOW-FAT DAIRY ☐ ☐ ☐
WHOLE GRAINS   LEAN PROTEINS
Non-fat dairy options are Power Foods and better for weight loss.

Day 5

	PointsPlus® value		POWER FOODS
	+/−	balance	▲
My daily **PointsPlus** Target:			
My remaining daily **PointsPlus** Target total:			
Activity **PointsPlus** values earned:			
Activity **PointsPlus** values used:			
Weekly **PointsPlus** Allowance used:			

My Activity Today:	Duration

GOOD HEALTH GUIDELINES

HAVE DAILY: LIQUIDS ☐ ☐ ☐ ☐ ☐ ☐
HEALTHY OILS ☐ ☐
MULTIVITAMIN ☐

ALSO REMEMBER: Watch your intake of sodium, added sugar, alcohol

EAT WEIGHT WATCHERS POWER FOODS

FRUITS & VEGGIES ☐ ☐ ☐ ☐ ☐ ☐ ☐ ☐ ☐
NON-FAT & LOW-FAT DAIRY ☐ ☐ ☐
WHOLE GRAINS   LEAN PROTEINS

Non-fat dairy options are Power Foods and better for weight loss.

Day 6

	PointsPlus® value		POWER FOODS ▲
	+/−	balance	
My daily **PointsPlus** Target:			
My remaining daily **PointsPlus** Target total:			▲
Activity **PointsPlus** values earned:			
Activity **PointsPlus** values used:			
Weekly **PointsPlus** Allowance used:			

My Activity Today:	Duration

GOOD HEALTH GUIDELINES

HAVE DAILY: LIQUIDS ☐ ☐ ☐ ☐ ☐ ☐
HEALTHY OILS ☐ ☐
MULTIVITAMIN ☐

ALSO REMEMBER: Watch your intake of sodium, added sugar, alcohol

EAT WEIGHT WATCHERS POWER FOODS

FRUITS & VEGGIES ☐ ☐ ☐ ☐ ☐ ☐ ☐ ☐ ☐
NON-FAT & LOW-FAT DAIRY ☐ ☐ ☐
WHOLE GRAINS   LEAN PROTEINS

Non-fat dairy options are Power Foods and better for weight loss.

	PointsPlus® value		POWER FOODS ▲
	+/−	balance	
My daily **PointsPlus** Target:			
My remaining daily **PointsPlus** Target total:			▲
Activity **PointsPlus** values earned:			
Activity **PointsPlus** values used:			
Weekly **PointsPlus** Allowance used:			
My Activity Today:		Duration	

GOOD HEALTH GUIDELINES

HAVE DAILY: LIQUIDS ☐ ☐ ☐ ☐ ☐ ☐
HEALTHY OILS ☐ ☐
MULTIVITAMIN ☐

ALSO REMEMBER: Watch your intake of sodium, added sugar, alcohol

EAT WEIGHT WATCHERS POWER FOODS

FRUITS & VEGGIES ☐ ☐ ☐ ☐ ☐ ☐ ☐ ☐ ☐
NON-FAT & LOW-FAT DAIRY ☐ ☐ ☐
WHOLE GRAINS   LEAN PROTEINS

Non-fat dairy options are Power Foods and better for weight loss.

Weekly Wrap-up

This week I lost/gained: _____

Meeting notes:

_____

_____

_____

_____

This week I learned:

_____

_____

_____

My Weekly *PointsPlus*® Allowance

49 48 47 46 45 44 43 42 41 40 39 38 37 36 35 34 33 32 31 30

29 28 27 26 25 24 23 22 21 20 19 18 17 16 15 14 13 12 11 10

9 8 7 6 5 4 3 2 1

My Weekly Activity *PointsPlus* Values

EARNED	1	2	3	4	5	6	7	8	9	10	11	12	13	14
USED	1	2	3	4	5	6	7	8	9	10	11	12	13	14
EARNED	15	16	17	18	19	20	21	22	23	24	25	26	27	28
USED	15	16	17	18	19	20	21	22	23	24	25	26	27	28
EARNED	29	30	31	32	33	34	35	36	37	38	39	40	41	42
USED	29	30	31	32	33	34	35	36	37	38	39	40	41	42

My Week at a Glance

	Day 1	Day 2	Day 3
What's coming this week			
Breakfast			
Lunch			
Dinner			
Snacks			
My Activity Plan			
Weekly *PointsPlus®* Allowance Allotted			

Date: /   /

Day 4	Day 5	Day 6	Day 7

My Weekly To Do List

notes

Dishes to Make:

Name of Dish: _____
_____

Where to find it: _____
_____

Name of Dish: _____
_____

Where to find it: _____
_____

Name of Dish: _____
_____

Where to find it: _____
_____

Name of Dish: _____
_____

Where to find it: _____
_____

Name of Dish: _____
_____

Where to find it: _____
_____

Groceries:

_____   _____
_____   _____
_____   _____
_____   _____
_____   _____
_____   _____
_____   _____
_____   _____
_____   _____
_____   _____
_____   _____
_____   _____
_____   _____
_____   _____
_____   _____
_____   _____
_____   _____

tip Don't just plan on getting your activity in at some point in the day. Make an actual appointment with yourself and schedule the start and stop time.

Date: / /

Day 1

| | PointsPlus® value | | POWER FOODS |
	+/−	balance	▲
My daily **PointsPlus** Target:			
My remaining daily **PointsPlus** Target total:			▲
Activity **PointsPlus** values earned:			
Activity **PointsPlus** values used:			
Weekly **PointsPlus** Allowance used:			

My Activity Today:	Duration

GOOD HEALTH GUIDELINES

HAVE DAILY: LIQUIDS ☐ ☐ ☐ ☐ ☐ ☐
HEALTHY OILS ☐ ☐
MULTIVITAMIN ☐

ALSO REMEMBER: Watch your intake of sodium, added sugar, alcohol

EAT WEIGHT WATCHERS POWER FOODS

FRUITS & VEGGIES ☐ ☐ ☐ ☐ ☐ ☐ ☐ ☐ ☐
NON-FAT & LOW-FAT DAIRY ☐ ☐ ☐
WHOLE GRAINS   LEAN PROTEINS

Non-fat dairy options are Power Foods and better for weight loss.

Day 2

| | PointsPlus® value | | POWER FOODS |
	+/−	balance	▲
My daily **PointsPlus** Target:			
My remaining daily **PointsPlus** Target total:			▲
Activity **PointsPlus** values earned:			
Activity **PointsPlus** values used:			
Weekly **PointsPlus** Allowance used:			
My Activity Today:		Duration	

GOOD HEALTH GUIDELINES

HAVE DAILY: LIQUIDS ☐ ☐ ☐ ☐ ☐ ☐
HEALTHY OILS ☐ ☐
MULTIVITAMIN ☐

ALSO REMEMBER: Watch your intake of sodium, added sugar, alcohol

EAT WEIGHT WATCHERS POWER FOODS

FRUITS & VEGGIES ☐ ☐ ☐ ☐ ☐ ☐ ☐ ☐ ☐
NON-FAT & LOW-FAT DAIRY ☐ ☐ ☐
WHOLE GRAINS   LEAN PROTEINS

Non-fat dairy options are Power Foods and better for weight loss.

Day 3

	PointsPlus® value		POWER FOODS ▲
	+/−	balance	
My daily **PointsPlus** Target:			
My remaining daily **PointsPlus** Target total:			▲
Activity **PointsPlus** values earned:			
Activity **PointsPlus** values used:			
Weekly **PointsPlus** Allowance used:			
My Activity Today:		Duration	

GOOD HEALTH GUIDELINES

HAVE DAILY: LIQUIDS ☐☐☐☐☐☐
HEALTHY OILS ☐☐
MULTIVITAMIN ☐
ALSO REMEMBER: Watch your intake of sodium, added sugar, alcohol

EAT WEIGHT WATCHERS POWER FOODS

FRUITS & VEGGIES ☐☐☐☐☐☐☐☐☐
NON-FAT & LOW-FAT DAIRY ☐☐☐
WHOLE GRAINS   LEAN PROTEINS
Non-fat dairy options are Power Foods and better for weight loss.

Day 4

	PointsPlus® value		POWER FOODS ▲
	+/–	balance	
My daily *PointsPlus* Target:			
My remaining daily *PointsPlus* Target total:			▲
Activity *PointsPlus* values earned:			
Activity *PointsPlus* values used:			
Weekly *PointsPlus* Allowance used:			

My Activity Today:	Duration

GOOD HEALTH GUIDELINES

HAVE DAILY: LIQUIDS ☐ ☐ ☐ ☐ ☐ ☐
HEALTHY OILS ☐ ☐
MULTIVITAMIN ☐

ALSO REMEMBER: Watch your intake of sodium, added sugar, alcohol

EAT WEIGHT WATCHERS POWER FOODS

FRUITS & VEGGIES ☐ ☐ ☐ ☐ ☐ ☐ ☐ ☐ ☐
NON-FAT & LOW-FAT DAIRY ☐ ☐ ☐
WHOLE GRAINS   LEAN PROTEINS

Non-fat dairy options are Power Foods and better for weight loss.

Day 5

	PointsPlus® value		POWER FOODS
	+/−	balance	▲
My daily *PointsPlus* Target:			
My remaining daily *PointsPlus* Target total:			▲
Activity *PointsPlus* values earned:			
Activity *PointsPlus* values used:			
Weekly *PointsPlus* Allowance used:			

My Activity Today:	Duration

GOOD HEALTH GUIDELINES

HAVE DAILY: LIQUIDS ☐ ☐ ☐ ☐ ☐ ☐
HEALTHY OILS ☐ ☐
MULTIVITAMIN ☐

ALSO REMEMBER: Watch your intake of sodium, added sugar, alcohol

EAT WEIGHT WATCHERS POWER FOODS

FRUITS & VEGGIES ☐ ☐ ☐ ☐ ☐ ☐ ☐ ☐ ☐
NON-FAT & LOW-FAT DAIRY ☐ ☐ ☐
WHOLE GRAINS   LEAN PROTEINS

Non-fat dairy options are Power Foods and better for weight loss.

Day 6

Date: /   /

10 week

	PointsPlus® value		POWER FOODS ▲
	+/−	balance	
My daily *PointsPlus* Target:			
My remaining daily *PointsPlus* Target total:			▲
Activity *PointsPlus* values earned:			
Activity *PointsPlus* values used:			
Weekly *PointsPlus* Allowance used:			
My Activity Today:		Duration	

GOOD HEALTH GUIDELINES

HAVE DAILY: LIQUIDS ☐ ☐ ☐ ☐ ☐ ☐
            HEALTHY OILS ☐ ☐
            MULTIVITAMIN ☐

ALSO REMEMBER: Watch your intake of sodium, added sugar, alcohol

EAT WEIGHT WATCHERS POWER FOODS

FRUITS & VEGGIES ☐ ☐ ☐ ☐ ☐ ☐ ☐ ☐ ☐ ☐
NON-FAT & LOW-FAT DAIRY ☐ ☐ ☐
WHOLE GRAINS   LEAN PROTEINS

Non-fat dairy options are Power Foods and better for weight loss.

Day 7

	PointsPlus® value		POWER FOODS ▲
	+/−	balance	
My daily *PointsPlus* Target:			
My remaining daily *PointsPlus* Target total:			▲
Activity *PointsPlus* values earned:			
Activity *PointsPlus* values used:			
Weekly *PointsPlus* Allowance used:			

My Activity Today:	Duration

GOOD HEALTH GUIDELINES

HAVE DAILY: LIQUIDS ☐ ☐ ☐ ☐ ☐ ☐
HEALTHY OILS ☐ ☐
MULTIVITAMIN ☐

ALSO REMEMBER: Watch your intake of sodium, added sugar, alcohol

EAT WEIGHT WATCHERS POWER FOODS

FRUITS & VEGGIES ☐ ☐ ☐ ☐ ☐ ☐ ☐ ☐ ☐
NON-FAT & LOW-FAT DAIRY ☐ ☐ ☐
WHOLE GRAINS   LEAN PROTEINS

Non-fat dairy options are Power Foods and better for weight loss.

Weekly Wrap-up

This week I lost/gained: _____

Meeting notes:

_____

_____

_____

_____

This week I learned:

_____

_____

_____

My Weekly *PointsPlus*® Allowance

49 48 47 46 45 44 43 42 41 40 39 38 37 36 35 34 33 32 31 30

29 28 27 26 25 24 23 22 21 20 19 18 17 16 15 14 13 12 11 10

9 8 7 6 5 4 3 2 1

My Weekly Activity *PointsPlus* Values

EARNED	1	2	3	4	5	6	7	8	9	10	11	12	13	14
USED	1	2	3	4	5	6	7	8	9	10	11	12	13	14
EARNED	15	16	17	18	19	20	21	22	23	24	25	26	27	28
USED	15	16	17	18	19	20	21	22	23	24	25	26	27	28
EARNED	29	30	31	32	33	34	35	36	37	38	39	40	41	42
USED	29	30	31	32	33	34	35	36	37	38	39	40	41	42

My Week at a Glance

	Day 1	Day 2	Day 3
What's coming this week			
Breakfast			
Lunch			
Dinner			
Snacks			
My Activity Plan			
Weekly *PointsPlus®* Allowance Allotted			

Day 4	Day 5	Day 6	Day 7

My Weekly To Do List

notes

Dishes to Make:

Name of Dish: _____
_____

Where to find it: _____
_____

Name of Dish: _____
_____

Where to find it: _____
_____

Name of Dish: _____
_____

Where to find it: _____
_____

Name of Dish: _____
_____

Where to find it: _____
_____

Name of Dish: _____
_____

Where to find it: _____
_____

Groceries:

_____   _____
_____   _____
_____   _____
_____   _____
_____   _____
_____   _____
_____   _____
_____   _____
_____   _____
_____   _____
_____   _____
_____   _____
_____   _____
_____   _____
_____   _____
_____   _____
_____   _____
_____   _____

tip No time to track what you are eating at the moment? Snap a picture with your smartphone and track when you get home!

Date: /   /

Day 1

	PointsPlus® value		POWER FOODS ▲
	+/−	balance	
My daily PointsPlus Target:			
My remaining daily PointsPlus Target total:			▲
Activity PointsPlus values earned:			
Activity PointsPlus values used:			
Weekly PointsPlus Allowance used:			
My Activity Today:		Duration	

GOOD HEALTH GUIDELINES

HAVE DAILY: LIQUIDS ☐☐☐☐☐☐
HEALTHY OILS ☐☐
MULTIVITAMIN ☐

ALSO REMEMBER: Watch your intake of sodium, added sugar, alcohol

EAT WEIGHT WATCHERS POWER FOODS

FRUITS & VEGGIES ☐☐☐☐☐☐☐☐☐
NON-FAT & LOW-FAT DAIRY ☐☐☐
WHOLE GRAINS   LEAN PROTEINS
Non-fat dairy options are Power Foods and better for weight loss.

	PointsPlus® value		POWER FOODS
	+/−	balance	▲
My daily *PointsPlus* Target:			
My remaining daily *PointsPlus* Target total:			
Activity *PointsPlus* values earned:			
Activity *PointsPlus* values used:			
Weekly *PointsPlus* Allowance used:			

My Activity Today:	Duration

GOOD HEALTH GUIDELINES

HAVE DAILY: LIQUIDS ☐ ☐ ☐ ☐ ☐ ☐
HEALTHY OILS ☐ ☐
MULTIVITAMIN ☐

ALSO REMEMBER: Watch your intake of sodium, added sugar, alcohol

EAT WEIGHT WATCHERS POWER FOODS

FRUITS & VEGGIES ☐ ☐ ☐ ☐ ☐ ☐ ☐ ☐ ☐
NON-FAT & LOW-FAT DAIRY ☐ ☐ ☐
WHOLE GRAINS   LEAN PROTEINS

Non-fat dairy options are Power Foods and better for weight loss.

Day 3

	PointsPlus® value		POWER FOODS
	+/−	balance	▲
My daily **PointsPlus** Target:			
My remaining daily **PointsPlus** Target total:			▲
Activity **PointsPlus** values earned:			
Activity **PointsPlus** values used:			
Weekly **PointsPlus** Allowance used:			
My Activity Today:		Duration	

GOOD HEALTH GUIDELINES

HAVE DAILY: LIQUIDS ☐ ☐ ☐ ☐ ☐ ☐
HEALTHY OILS ☐ ☐
MULTIVITAMIN ☐

ALSO REMEMBER: Watch your intake of sodium, added sugar, alcohol

EAT WEIGHT WATCHERS POWER FOODS

FRUITS & VEGGIES ☐ ☐ ☐ ☐ ☐ ☐ ☐ ☐ ☐
NON-FAT & LOW-FAT DAIRY ☐ ☐ ☐
WHOLE GRAINS   LEAN PROTEINS

Non-fat dairy options are Power Foods and better for weight loss.

	PointsPlus® value		POWER FOODS ▲
	+/−	balance	
My daily PointsPlus Target:			
My remaining daily PointsPlus Target total:			▲
Activity PointsPlus values earned:			
Activity PointsPlus values used			
Weekly PointsPlus Allowance used:			

My Activity Today:	Duration

GOOD HEALTH GUIDELINES

HAVE DAILY: LIQUIDS ☐☐☐☐☐☐
HEALTHY OILS ☐☐
MULTIVITAMIN ☐

ALSO REMEMBER: Watch your intake of sodium, added sugar, alcohol

EAT WEIGHT WATCHERS POWER FOODS

FRUITS & VEGGIES ☐☐☐☐☐☐☐☐☐
NON-FAT & LOW-FAT DAIRY ☐☐☐
WHOLE GRAINS LEAN PROTEINS

Non-fat dairy options are Power Foods and better for weight loss.

Day 5

	PointsPlus® value		POWER FOODS ▲
	+/−	balance	
My daily PointsPlus Target:			
My remaining daily PointsPlus Target total:			
Activity PointsPlus values earned:			
Activity PointsPlus values used:			
Weekly PointsPlus Allowance used:			

My Activity Today:	Duration

GOOD HEALTH GUIDELINES

HAVE DAILY: LIQUIDS ☐☐☐☐☐☐
HEALTHY OILS ☐☐
MULTIVITAMIN ☐

ALSO REMEMBER: Watch your intake of sodium, added sugar, alcohol

EAT WEIGHT WATCHERS POWER FOODS

FRUITS & VEGGIES ☐☐☐☐☐☐☐☐☐
NON-FAT & LOW-FAT DAIRY ☐☐☐
WHOLE GRAINS   LEAN PROTEINS

Non-fat dairy options are Power Foods and better for weight loss.

Day 6

	PointsPlus® value		POWER FOODS
	+/−	balance	▲
My daily PointsPlus Target:			
My remaining daily PointsPlus Target total:			▲
Activity PointsPlus values earned:			
Activity PointsPlus values used:			
Weekly PointsPlus Allowance used:			

My Activity Today:	Duration

GOOD HEALTH GUIDELINES

HAVE DAILY: LIQUIDS ☐ ☐ ☐ ☐ ☐ ☐
HEALTHY OILS ☐ ☐
MULTIVITAMIN ☐

ALSO REMEMBER: Watch your intake of sodium, added sugar, alcohol

EAT WEIGHT WATCHERS POWER FOODS

FRUITS & VEGGIES ☐ ☐ ☐ ☐ ☐ ☐ ☐ ☐ ☐
NON-FAT & LOW-FAT DAIRY ☐ ☐ ☐
WHOLE GRAINS   LEAN PROTEINS

Non-fat dairy options are Power Foods and better for weight loss.

Day 7

	PointsPlus® value		POWER FOODS ▲
	+/−	balance	
My daily PointsPlus Target:			
My remaining daily PointsPlus Target total:			▲
Activity PointsPlus values earned:			
Activity PointsPlus values used:			
Weekly PointsPlus Allowance used:			

My Activity Today:	Duration

GOOD HEALTH GUIDELINES

HAVE DAILY: **LIQUIDS** ☐ ☐ ☐ ☐ ☐ ☐
HEALTHY OILS ☐ ☐
MULTIVITAMIN ☐

ALSO REMEMBER: Watch your intake of sodium, added sugar, alcohol

EAT WEIGHT WATCHERS POWER FOODS

FRUITS & VEGGIES ☐ ☐ ☐ ☐ ☐ ☐ ☐ ☐ ☐
NON-FAT & LOW-FAT DAIRY ☐ ☐ ☐
WHOLE GRAINS   LEAN PROTEINS

Non-fat dairy options are Power Foods and better for weight loss.

Weekly Wrap-up

This week I lost/gained: _____

Meeting notes:

_____

_____

_____

_____

This week I learned:

_____

_____

_____

My Weekly *PointsPlus®* Allowance

49 48 47 46 45 44 43 42 41 40 39 38 37 36 35 34 33 32 31 30

29 28 27 26 25 24 23 22 21 20 19 18 17 16 15 14 13 12 11 10

9 8 7 6 5 4 3 2 1

My Weekly Activity *PointsPlus* Values

EARNED	1	2	3	4	5	6	7	8	9	10	11	12	13	14
USED	1	2	3	4	5	6	7	8	9	10	11	12	13	14
EARNED	15	16	17	18	19	20	21	22	23	24	25	26	27	28
USED	15	16	17	18	19	20	21	22	23	24	25	26	27	28
EARNED	29	30	31	32	33	34	35	36	37	38	39	40	41	42
USED	29	30	31	32	33	34	35	36	37	38	39	40	41	42

My Week at a Glance

	Day 1	Day 2	Day 3
What's coming this week			
Breakfast			
Lunch			
Dinner			
Snacks			
My Activity Plan			
Weekly *PointsPlus®* Allowance Allotted			

Day 4	Day 5	Day 6	Day 7

My Weekly To Do List

notes

Dishes to Make:

Name of Dish: _____

_____

Where to find it: _____

_____

Name of Dish: _____

_____

Where to find it: _____

_____

Name of Dish: _____

_____

Where to find it: _____

_____

Name of Dish: _____

_____

Where to find it: _____

_____

Name of Dish: _____

_____

Where to find it: _____

_____

Groceries:

_____   _____
_____   _____
_____   _____
_____   _____
_____   _____
_____   _____
_____   _____
_____   _____
_____   _____
_____   _____
_____   _____
_____   _____
_____   _____
_____   _____
_____   _____
_____   _____
_____   _____
_____   _____

 tip Congratulate yourself. The fact that you have stayed with the Plan and this book for 12 weeks is an accomplishment all by itself.

Day 1

| | PointsPlus® value | | POWER FOODS ▲ |
	+/–	balance	
My daily **PointsPlus** Target:			
My remaining daily **PointsPlus** Target total:			▲
Activity **PointsPlus** values earned:			
Activity **PointsPlus** values used:			
Weekly **PointsPlus** Allowance used:			

My Activity Today:	Duration

GOOD HEALTH GUIDELINES

HAVE DAILY: LIQUIDS ☐ ☐ ☐ ☐ ☐ ☐
 HEALTHY OILS ☐ ☐
 MULTIVITAMIN ☐

ALSO REMEMBER: Watch your intake of sodium, added sugar, alcohol

EAT WEIGHT WATCHERS POWER FOODS

FRUITS & VEGGIES ☐ ☐ ☐ ☐ ☐ ☐ ☐ ☐ ☐
NON-FAT & LOW-FAT DAIRY ☐ ☐ ☐
WHOLE GRAINS   LEAN PROTEINS

Non-fat dairy options are Power Foods and better for weight loss.

Day 2

	PointsPlus® value		POWER FOODS
	+/−	balance	▲
My daily PointsPlus Target:			
My remaining daily PointsPlus Target total:			▲
Activity PointsPlus values earned:			
Activity PointsPlus values used:			
Weekly PointsPlus Allowance used:			
My Activity Today:		Duration	

GOOD HEALTH GUIDELINES

HAVE DAILY: LIQUIDS ☐ ☐ ☐ ☐ ☐ ☐
HEALTHY OILS ☐ ☐
MULTIVITAMIN ☐

ALSO REMEMBER: Watch your intake of sodium, added sugar, alcohol

EAT WEIGHT WATCHERS POWER FOODS

FRUITS & VEGGIES ☐ ☐ ☐ ☐ ☐ ☐ ☐ ☐ ☐
NON-FAT & LOW-FAT DAIRY ☐ ☐ ☐
WHOLE GRAINS   LEAN PROTEINS

Non-fat dairy options are Power Foods and better for weight loss.

Day 3

	PointsPlus® value		POWER FOODS ▲
	+/−	balance	
My daily **PointsPlus** Target:			
My remaining daily **PointsPlus** Target total:			▲
Activity **PointsPlus** values earned:			
Activity **PointsPlus** values used:			
Weekly **PointsPlus** Allowance used:			
My Activity Today:		Duration	

GOOD HEALTH GUIDELINES

HAVE DAILY: LIQUIDS ☐ ☐ ☐ ☐ ☐ ☐
    HEALTHY OILS ☐ ☐
    MULTIVITAMIN ☐

ALSO REMEMBER: Watch your intake of sodium, added sugar, alcohol

EAT WEIGHT WATCHERS POWER FOODS

FRUITS & VEGGIES ☐ ☐ ☐ ☐ ☐ ☐ ☐ ☐ ☐
NON-FAT & LOW-FAT DAIRY ☐ ☐ ☐
WHOLE GRAINS   LEAN PROTEINS

Non-fat dairy options are Power Foods and better for weight loss.

Day 4

| | PointsPlus® value | | POWER FOODS ▲ |
	+/-	balance	
My daily PointsPlus Target:			
My remaining daily PointsPlus Target total:			▲
Activity PointsPlus values earned:			
Activity PointsPlus values used:			
Weekly PointsPlus Allowance used:			
My Activity Today:		Duration	

GOOD HEALTH GUIDELINES

HAVE DAILY: LIQUIDS ☐ ☐ ☐ ☐ ☐ ☐
             HEALTHY OILS ☐ ☐
             MULTIVITAMIN ☐

ALSO REMEMBER: Watch your intake of sodium, added sugar, alcohol

EAT WEIGHT WATCHERS POWER FOODS

FRUITS & VEGGIES ☐ ☐ ☐ ☐ ☐ ☐ ☐ ☐ ☐
NON-FAT & LOW-FAT DAIRY ☐ ☐ ☐
WHOLE GRAINS   LEAN PROTEINS

Non-fat dairy options are Power Foods and better for weight loss.

Day 5

	PointsPlus® value		POWER FOODS ▲
	+/−	balance	
My daily **PointsPlus** Target:			
My remaining daily **PointsPlus** Target total:			▲
Activity **PointsPlus** values earned:			
Activity **PointsPlus** values used:			
Weekly **PointsPlus** Allowance used:			
My Activity Today:		Duration	

GOOD HEALTH GUIDELINES

HAVE DAILY: LIQUIDS ☐ ☐ ☐ ☐ ☐ ☐
HEALTHY OILS ☐ ☐
MULTIVITAMIN ☐
ALSO REMEMBER: Watch your intake of sodium, added sugar, alcohol

EAT WEIGHT WATCHERS POWER FOODS

FRUITS & VEGGIES ☐ ☐ ☐ ☐ ☐ ☐ ☐ ☐
NON-FAT & LOW-FAT DAIRY ☐ ☐ ☐
WHOLE GRAINS   LEAN PROTEINS
Non-fat dairy options are Power Foods and better for weight loss.

Day 6

| | PointsPlus® value | | POWER FOODS |
	+/−	balance	▲
My daily **PointsPlus** Target:			
My remaining daily **PointsPlus** Target total:			▲
Activity **PointsPlus** values earned:			
Activity **PointsPlus** values used:			
Weekly **PointsPlus** Allowance used:			
My Activity Today:		Duration	

GOOD HEALTH GUIDELINES

HAVE DAILY: LIQUIDS ☐ ☐ ☐ ☐ ☐ ☐
HEALTHY OILS ☐ ☐
MULTIVITAMIN ☐

ALSO REMEMBER: Watch your intake of sodium, added sugar, alcohol

EAT WEIGHT WATCHERS POWER FOODS

FRUITS & VEGGIES ☐ ☐ ☐ ☐ ☐ ☐ ☐ ☐ ☐
NON-FAT & LOW-FAT DAIRY ☐ ☐ ☐
WHOLE GRAINS   LEAN PROTEINS

Non-fat dairy options are Power Foods and better for weight loss.

Day 7

	PointsPlus° value		POWER FOODS ▲
	+/−	balance	
My daily **PointsPlus** Target:			
My remaining daily **PointsPlus** Target total:			▲
Activity **PointsPlus** values earned:			
Activity **PointsPlus** values used:			
Weekly **PointsPlus** Allowance used:			
My Activity Today:		Duration	

GOOD HEALTH GUIDELINES

HAVE DAILY: LIQUIDS ☐☐☐☐☐☐
HEALTHY OILS ☐☐
MULTIVITAMIN ☐

ALSO REMEMBER: Watch your intake of sodium, added sugar, alcohol

EAT WEIGHT WATCHERS POWER FOODS

FRUITS & VEGGIES ☐☐☐☐☐☐☐☐☐
NON-FAT & LOW-FAT DAIRY ☐☐☐
WHOLE GRAINS   LEAN PROTEINS

Non-fat dairy options are Power Foods and better for weight loss.

Weekly Wrap-up

This week I lost/gained: _____

Meeting notes:

_____

_____

_____

_____

This week I learned:

_____

_____

_____

My Weekly *PointsPlus*® Allowance

49 48 47 46 45 44 43 42 41 40 39 38 37 36 35 34 33 32 31 30

29 28 27 26 25 24 23 22 21 20 19 18 17 16 15 14 13 12 11 10

9 8 7 6 5 4 3 2 1

My Weekly Activity *PointsPlus* Values

EARNED	1	2	3	4	5	6	7	8	9	10	11	12	13	14
USED	1	2	3	4	5	6	7	8	9	10	11	12	13	14
EARNED	15	16	17	18	19	20	21	22	23	24	25	26	27	28
USED	15	16	17	18	19	20	21	22	23	24	25	26	27	28
EARNED	29	30	31	32	33	34	35	36	37	38	39	40	41	42
USED	29	30	31	32	33	34	35	36	37	38	39	40	41	42

notes

notes

notes

notes

notes